THE MOON

For Mia, who I love to the Moon and beyond...
and for Mike, who is our shining beam of light.
~ H.P.

For Opa and Ella.

~ T.H.

THE MOON

by
Hannah Pang

illustrated by
Thomas Hegbrook

Contents

"The Moon is the first milestone on the road to the stars."

– Arthur C. Clarke, author

F or many thousands of years, humankind has looked up to the skies in awe, gazing in wonder at the Moon. It has inspired people the world over, from storytellers, poets and scientists to musicians, mathematicians and dreamers...

But while the Moon has been a constant in our night sky, our view of it has been ever-changing: from the magical idea of it as a god to the belief that it was covered in seas – and even plants!

In this book we'll explore the reasons why the Moon continues to be a source of fascination and flights of fancy well into the 21st century. On our journey, we will discover the extent of the Moon's influence on all of our lives, examine some of the myths and legends surrounding it and try to separate the fact from the fiction.

CHAPTER **ONE**

Many
Moons
Ago

A Moon or a Planet?

Our Moon is not alone! In fact, there are millions of moons in the universe. There are also millions of planets. But what makes a moon a moon and a planet a planet?

While both planets and moons can be made up of a mixture of rock and metal, there is one main difference that sets them apart:

Moons orbit planets, while planets orbit stars.

To understand this, it might help to think about our own planet, Earth, in relation to our own Moon and the Sun (which is in fact a star, or a big ball of gas).

In the 3rd century BCE, an astronomer called Aristarchus of Samos in Greece came up with the idea that planet Earth travels around the Sun. Until then, people believed that the Sun, Moon, stars and planets all travelled around Earth – we really did believe that we were the centre of everything! People took some convincing that this Greek astronomer was right, but eventually his idea was accepted.

Gradually astronomers began to realise that the Sun, although at the centre of Earth's solar system, was not actually at the centre of the universe. The term 'solar system' first appeared in the English language around 1704. The solar system is the collection of eight planets plus their moons, along with asteroids, comets and other space debris, which all revolve around our Sun.

So we now know that Earth travels around the Sun, and takes about 365 days, or one year, to do so.

And – thanks to Sir Isaac Newton – we also know that the Moon travels around Earth. In the 1660s, this English mathematician and physicist was the first to work out that the force of gravity keeps the Moon in orbit around our planet – taking 27.32 Earth days to complete a full circuit.

As Old As Time?

Where Did the Moon Come From?

Was the Moon formed at the same time as Earth, from clouds of dust and gas? Astronomer Galileo Galilei's telescope showed that the Moon had mountains and plains just like Earth, so perhaps they somehow formed alongside each other?

A Part of Us?

Was the Moon a part of Earth that simply spun off? In the 1800s, George Darwin, the son of famous English naturalist and geologist Charles Darwin, suggested that when the Earth was very young, it rotated very quickly – possibly causing part of it to fly off into space and become the Moon. He believed the Pacific Ocean was the mark left behind on Earth after this event.

The Pull of Gravity

In the early 1950s, American scientist Harold Urey speculated that the Moon had formed elsewhere in the solar system and was then captured by Earth's gravity. When objects are captured, the speed of their rotation slows down. So the Earth caused the Moon's rotation to slow to match the speed of the Moon's orbit, which is why we only see one side of it.

However, there have been many arguments against these theories. The materials that the Moon is made from are similar to Earth's, but not identical. Some say there is not enough geological evidence to suggest that the Moon was once a part of Earth or formed at the same time, while others are doubtful that the Moon would have slowed down enough to be captured by gravity – and why didn't it then collide with Earth?

The Big Splash

Nobody can be sure what happened, but most scientists agree that the Moon had a fiery beginning. In 1975, William Hartmann and Donald R. Davis of the Planetary Science Institute in Arizona, USA, came up with a new theory...

About 4.5 billion years ago, a meandering planet about half the size of Earth, called Theia, collided with Earth. The cataclysmic force blasted large chunks of rock from both planets in an extremely hot vapour. The gas, rock and dust were captured in orbit around Earth, before cooling rapidly and eventually being drawn together into a ball by gravity. And so the Moon was born.

Vital Statistics

The Moon orbits the Earth day in and day out – an ever-moving picture that gradually changes shape in the sky… but how much do we really know about the Moon?

We know that it is about 4.5 billion years old but exactly how big is it? Just over 2,300 years ago Aristarchus of Samos timed how long the Moon took to travel through the Earth's shadow – helping him to work out the diameters of both Earth and the Moon. Although smaller than Earth, at about one-quarter of its diameter, our Moon is the fifth largest of 181 moons in the solar system. Its diameter is about 3,476km (2,160mi); its circumference around the equator is about 10,921km (6,786mi); and its surface area is about 38 million km^2 (14.7 million mi^2).

Good Neighbours?

They may be neighbours, but the Moon and Earth are quite different. Planet Earth is quite 'active' with its ever-shifting tectonic plates. Tectonic plates are layers within Earth's crust that jostle about, creating mountains, volcanoes and earthquakes.

By contrast, the Moon is a lifeless, airless ball of rock – cloaked with a layer of dust. With no atmosphere or weather, the Moon's surface has remained the same for more than a billion years since most of its volcanoes stopped bubbling over and since large impacts by meteoroids or asteroids became rarer! In fact, the footprints made by the twelve Apollo astronauts who landed on the Moon between the years of 1969–72 will still be there now and are likely to be there for millions of years to come.

Creating an Atmosphere

Earth's gravity is strong enough to capture a big cloud of gases, or atmosphere, creating the right combination of pressure and temperature to allow seas to flow.

But the Moon has only one-sixth of the Earth's gravity, which results in a very thin atmosphere. This means that any water evaporates into space and leaves it as dry as a bone – apart from the spots of ice dotted around its north and south poles.

The Moon's thin atmosphere provides no protection from hot days and can't hold in heat at night. Temperatures can therefore be as high as 123°C (253°F) and can drop to −233°C (−387°F). Brrrr…

Keeping Your Feet on the Ground

So what exactly is gravity? Gravity is an invisible force of attraction that pulls objects together. The greater an object's mass (the amount of matter, or physical substance it contains), the greater the gravitational pull. On Earth it is gravity that keeps our feet on the ground. But out in space, gravity is the force that pulls planets in orbit around stars, and which keeps the Moon in orbit around our very own planet…

Legend has it that Sir Isaac Newton came up with this theory of gravity when an apple dropped from a tree and hit him on the head. He probably noticed that the apple accelerated (or sped up) from a resting position as it fell, and that to accelerate, an object must have a force applied to it: in this case the force was gravity. He showed that the force that pulled the apple to the ground was the same force that pulls the Moon into orbit around Earth.

Gravity on

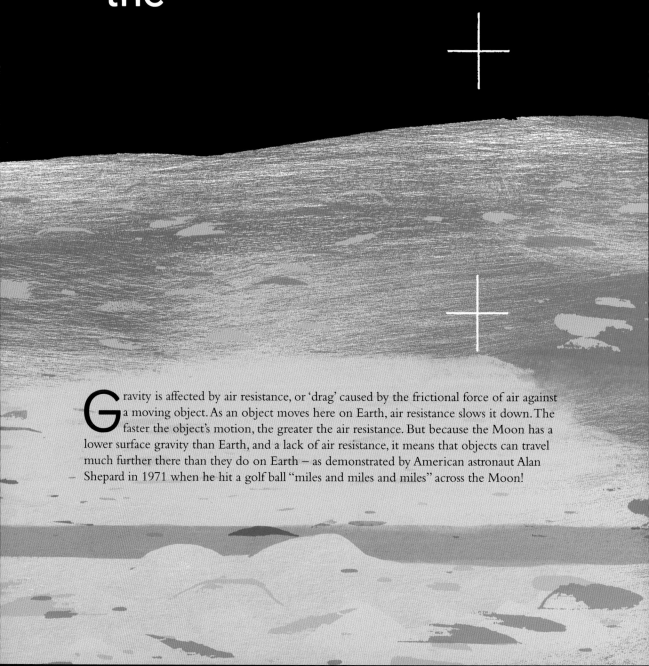

the

Gravity is affected by air resistance, or 'drag' caused by the frictional force of air against a moving object. As an object moves here on Earth, air resistance slows it down. The faster the object's motion, the greater the air resistance. But because the Moon has a lower surface gravity than Earth, and a lack of air resistance, it means that objects can travel much further there than they do on Earth – as demonstrated by American astronaut Alan Shepard in 1971 when he hit a golf ball "miles and miles and miles" across the Moon!

Raven and How the Tides Began

A Tlingit legend

*L*ong ago, when the world was new, Raven and his people lived by the shore of the Big Water. The people would eat any food that washed up along the shore, but they could not go out into the Big Water, because it was very deep and there were no tides.

Raven was always hungry and loved to eat the food that he found on the shore. But as time went by, there were more and more people and Raven began to worry that there would not be enough food to go around.

Soon Raven fell into a deep sleep. In his dreams a Great Spirit came to him saying, "Raven, I have seen that your people do not have enough food to eat. At the edge of the Big Water, at the end of the world, there is a cave. In this cave lives an old woman who holds the tide line, controlling the rising and falling of the water. She holds on to this line very tightly. If you can get her to let go of the line, the water will fall and your people will be able to get food from the Big Water. You must find a way to trick the old lady into letting go of the line."

When Raven awoke from his dream he knew what he must do. Raven flew for four days and nights until finally he came to the cave at the edge of the Big Water. Raven saw the old woman sitting in the cave holding tightly to the line across her lap.

Raven strutted up and down in front of the cave, rubbing his belly and saying loudly, "Mmm, those clams were so good!" The old woman heard Raven and called to him, "Raven! Where did you get those clams?" Raven did not reply but strutted in front of the cave, again rubbing his belly and boasting about the clams. The woman leaned out of her cave and called out again, "Raven! Where did you get those clams?"

Still Raven did not reply. Instead, he continued to strut in front of the cave, exclaiming, "Mmm! I wish I had more of those clams!" The old woman leaned further forward and, as quick as a flash, Raven kicked sand up into the woman's eyes. Blinded, she tried to brush the sand away and as she did so, she let go of the line!

The waters fell back, uncovering some of the Big Water. Raven flew home dreaming of all of the tasty things that he would soon be eating. Raven's people were delighted and held a huge feast to celebrate.

For many days, the people ate all the good things from the Big Water. But then a terrible thing happened. Many of the creatures from the Big Water began to die. They washed up on the shore and began to rot and smell. The people went to Raven to beg for his help.

So Raven flew for four days and nights back to the old woman in her cave. When Raven arrived he found the old woman still trying to get the sand out of her eyes. "Raven!" she called, "Is that you? You tricked me! Help me get the sand out of my eyes, and find the tide line!"

Raven said, "Yes, I did trick you into letting go of the line so that the waters would fall and we could get food from the Big Water. But now, the creatures of the Big Water are dying, and my people have nothing to eat. If I help you, will you help my people by letting go of the tide line from time to time? Then we will be able to get some of the good things to eat from the Big Water. And the creatures of the Big Water will not die because they are not covered by the waters that are their home."

The old woman immediately agreed. So Raven cleared the sand out of the woman's eyes and gave her the tide line to hold on to again. And from that day onwards the woman would let go of the line from time to time to allow the waters to fall back. Raven's people now had plenty to eat and gave thanks to Raven for helping them. And that is the story of how the tides began.

The Pull of the Tides

J ust as Earth's gravity keeps the Moon in its orbit, the Moon's gravity pulls on Earth. It causes the oceans to bulge out in the direction of the Moon, creating tides. The ocean directly facing the Moon bulges towards the Moon with the pull of the Moon's gravity. The ocean on the other side of Earth also bulges as the Moon gently pulls Earth away from the water on that side. And because Earth rotates once on its own axis every 24 hours, we move through one of those two bulges every twelve hours, meaning we get two high tides and two low tides a day.

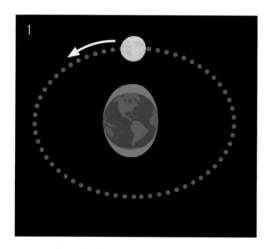
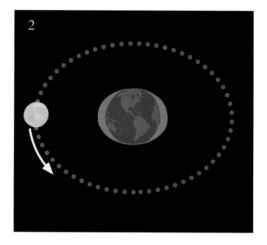
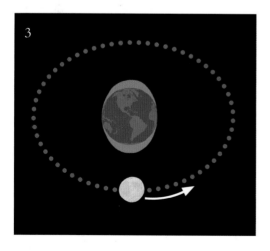
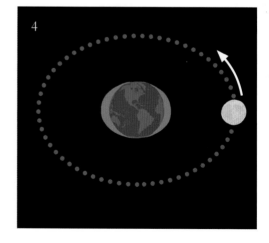

A spring tide is when the water 'springs' higher or lower. Like the Moon, the Sun also pulls on Earth and its oceans, but not as strongly as it is so far away. During a new or full Moon, the Sun, Moon and Earth are lined up in a row so the Sun adds to the gravitational pull on the oceans, making the tides higher or lower.

Neap tides occur seven days after a spring tide – this is when high tides are a little lower and low tides are a little higher than average. They happen because the Sun and Moon are at right angles to each other. When the Sun and the Moon are both pulling at Earth from different angles like this, they essentially cancel out each other's pull on the bulge of the ocean, evening it out a little.

On average, the Moon is about 384,400km (238,855mi) away from us.
At its furthest point, it's about 405,696km (252,088mi) away.
At its closest, it's about 363,105km (225,623mi).

So Near, Yet So Far

We have discovered that the Moon orbits around Earth, but did you know that the path it takes is not quite circular? It is more of an oval shape. And for this reason, sometimes it is closer to Earth than at other times.

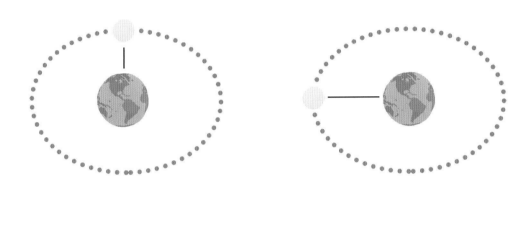

We know that the Moon takes 27.32 Earth days to complete its orbit and it takes a similar amount of time to complete one spin on its axis. The rate at which it rotates on its axis is the same rate at which it orbits Earth, and this is the reason why we only ever see one side of the Moon.

The time it takes for the Moon to rotate on its axis is essentially a lunar day. So one day on the Moon is really equivalent to about one month on Earth!

Moone to Moon

The word 'Moon' can actually be traced back to the Old English word, *mōna* – meaning 'month'. This shows just how far back people's association between the Moon and the recording of time goes. And there are many other languages that have similar words for it. By the 15th century, English-speaking people began calling it the Moon, although it was often spelled 'Moone'.

Shining Light on the Subject

W e all tend to think of the Moon as shining in the sky. Of course, the Moon only *appears* to shine. The light that the Moon gives off is simply a reflection of the Sun's own light. Anaxagoras, a Greek philosopher living in around 510–428BCE, is said to have been the first person to discover this. He also thought that Earth was flat, but perhaps you can't get everything right all of the time…

The Moon appears to change shape as it orbits the Earth, because at certain points in its journey it catches more of the Sun's light than at others and we can only see the parts that are lit up. This is what is meant by 'phases of the Moon' – it is the different phases, or shapes, that can be seen over the course of a month. From Earth we see different amounts of the near side of the Moon, depending on how far it has travelled in its orbit.

It takes roughly 29.5 days for the Moon to go from one new Moon to another new Moon – this is called the synodic month. But it only takes 27.32 days for the Moon to complete its orbit around Earth (known as the sidereal month). This is because as the Earth is constantly moving along its orbit around the Sun, the Moon must travel slightly further to get from one new Moon to the next – it is constantly playing 'catch-up' with Earth.

If you were to stand on the near side of the Moon, you would see Earth phases, just like Moon phases, moving from total darkness, to crescents, full Earth, and back again. However, the face of Earth would be constantly changing as it spins.

We might see slightly different 'halves' of the Moon at different times – this is because the Moon sometimes rocks slowly back and forth, showing us a marginally different angle – this motion is known as lunar libration.

sunlight

1. *New Moon*
The Moon's far side faces the Sun. Its near side is in darkness so we cannot see the Moon from Earth.

2. *Waxing crescent*
The Moon is waxing (it appears to grow) as part of the near side can be seen from Earth.

8. *Waning crescent*
Only a thin sliver of the Moon can now be seen from Earth – it has nearly waned.

3. *First quarter*
This stage is so named because the Moon has completed a quarter of its orbit. Now you can see half of the Moon's near side from Earth.

7. *Last quarter*
A quarter of the Moon's orbit remains. But half of the Moon's near side can be seen from Earth.

4. *Waxing gibbous*
The Moon looks bright and nearly full.

6. *Waning gibbous*
The Moon is waning (it appears to shrink).

5. *Full Moon*
The Moon's near side is in direct line with the Sun.

The Harvest Moon

by Henry Wadsworth Longfellow

It is the Harvest Moon! On gilded vanes
And roofs of villages, on woodland crests
And their aerial neighbourhoods of nests
Deserted, on the curtained window-panes
Of rooms where children sleep, on country lanes
And harvest-fields, its mystic splendour rests!
Gone are the birds that were our summer guests,
With the last sheaves return the labouring wains!
All things are symbols: the external shows
Of Nature have their image in the mind,
As flowers and fruits and falling of the leaves;
The song-birds leave us at the summer's close,
Only the empty nests are left behind,
And pipings of the quail among the sheaves.

Exceptional Moons

The Moon spends about half of its time crossing our daytime skies. The main reason that we are able to see the Moon during the day is that the time it takes for the Moon to orbit around Earth is different from the time it takes for the Earth to make one full rotation on its axis.

And just like sunrise and sunset, the time that the Moon rises and sets changes each day too. If the Moon stayed in one fixed position in the sky, we would probably see it at the same time each night as the Earth spins once on its own axis. But because the Moon moves on its own orbital course, we see it in a different spot each night.

Harvest Moon

Our Moon appears to have many changing faces. The harvest Moon is the full Moon that occurs nearest to the start of the autumnal equinox – the start of autumn in the Northern Hemisphere. This usually occurs around 22nd or 23rd September. Equinox means 'equal night'; so at this point in the year both night and day are roughly the same in length. The full harvest Moon rises at sunset. Throughout history, such bright moonlight in the early evening helped farmers to harvest their crops, hence the name.

Massive Moons

Hunters' Moon

In late October in the Northern Hemisphere you might spot the hunters' Moon. The name of this full Moon can be traced back to the First Nations of North America. The bright autumn moonlight helped the First Nations to hunt deer so that they could stock up on food before winter.

And so the hunter's Moon is associated with feasting. The 'Feast of the Hunters' Moon' was a feast day held by Native American tribes and by some people in Western Europe as long ago as the 1700s. The 'Feast of the Hunters' Moon' has been revived and is now a yearly festival in West Lafayette, Indiana in late September or early October.

Supermoons

The definition of a supermoon is a new Moon or a full Moon at its closest point to Earth during the Moon's monthly orbit. Astrologer, Richard Nolle, came up with the term 'supermoon' in 1979, although his description was a little more technical. A supermoon at its brightest and fullest is a spectacular sight to behold!

Blue moons

The phrase 'once in a blue Moon' is used to describe something that happens only rarely. In our skies, a blue Moon is an unusual event when an extra full Moon appears within a certain time frame. According to an old North American farmer's journal, published in August 1937:

"We usually see a full Moon twelve times in a year, three times for each season. But occasionally, there will be a year that has thirteen full Moons, meaning that one of the four seasons contains four full Moons instead of the usual three."

Though this kind of full Moon is not actually blue, certain air conditions after volcanic eruptions or fires can leave particles in the air, which can make a Moon *appear* blue. And this kind of blue Moon is a very rare sight indeed!

Eclipse Legends

The Mesopotamians thought an eclipse meant that the Moon was under attack from seven demons. They saw it as an attack on their king, so for the period of an eclipse, they would instal a stand-in king who would be the target of any attack. Once the eclipse was over, the substitute king was regarded as expendable and would usually mysteriously disappear.

The Hupa Native American tribe believed that the Moon had 20 wives and many pets, such as mountain lions and snakes. If the Moon didn't give its pets enough food they would attack the Moon and make it bleed. But the Moon's wives would come to its aid, clearing up the blood, and the eclipse would end.

The Batammaliba people of Togo and Benin believed that the Sun and Moon were locked in a never-ending struggle and each eclipse was a battle in that war – showing what could happen if you let your differences fester. As a result, the Batammaliba saw the eclipse as a time to make peace with their neighbours.

The Incas feared that an eclipse was caused by a jaguar attacking the Moon. They thought that, after attacking the Moon, the jaguar would fall to Earth and start eating the people. In order to scare the jaguar off, they would make as much noise as possible, shaking their spears and getting their dogs to howl.

Moon Shadows

Lunar eclipses take place during a full Moon when the Sun, Earth and Moon are lined up in a row. As Earth gradually moves between the Moon and the Sun, Earth's shadow creeps across the face of the Moon, turning it an eerie red. This red colour is in fact the Sun's light after it has travelled through the edge of Earth's atmosphere, causing the light to bend and scatter.

Crafty Columbus

In the past, people did not understand the science behind lunar eclipses and believed that they were signs of evil. The Spanish explorer Christopher Columbus used this to his advantage when he became stranded with his crew in Jamaica in 1504. Knowing that there would be a total eclipse of the Moon on 29th February, he managed to scare the local people into helping with his rescue. He persuaded them that God was angry and that the Moon would only return to normal if they helped him.

A solar eclipse occurs when the Moon passes between Earth and the Sun, blocking out the Sun and casting a shadow on part of Earth's surface. The Moon's shadow is not big enough to cover the whole of Earth so only a small area of Earth will see a total eclipse while people outside of the shadowed area will see a partial eclipse.

Off with their heads!

It must have been a frightening sight in ancient times when the Sun grew dark during the daytime – many people thought it was a sign of the Apocalypse (the end of the world). In ancient China, predicting eclipses was the job of astronomers. One of the earliest recordings of a total solar eclipse comes from 2134BCE, when two Chinese astronomers failed to predict it. As a result, they had their heads chopped off!

Solar eclipses, either partial or total, usually only happen once or twice a year, although up to seven lunar and solar eclipses *can* fall in any one year.

Picture This...

The Moon has inspired many tales over time – and not all have been linked to evil or catastrophe. In the Western world, people often imagine that they see the Man in the Moon, while those in the East often see a rabbit or a hare.

Seeing seas

The surface of the Moon is covered with dark and light areas. The dark areas are actually solidified beds of lava from when the Moon's volcanoes were still active (most of these lava flows erupted between 3.5 and 1 billion years ago). These large lava beds are called *maria*, which is the Latin word for 'seas' – because early astronomers mistook them for bodies of water.

The smaller dark areas are made up of rocky craters varying from a few metres across to hundreds of kilometres. These were created by large meteoroids or asteroids that melted parts of the Moon's surface when they collided with it. Some of these craters were then filled in with volcanic lava, creating the dark areas that you can see.

The light areas on the Moon are lunar highlands, or mountains. There are eighteen mountain ranges on the Moon and many valleys. The highest point on the Moon is called the Selenean summit. Measuring 10,786m (35,387ft) above the Moon's surface, it rises higher than Mount Everest on Earth, which measures 8,848m (29,029ft) above sea level.

Moon Markings

On the dark side

The Selenean summit is located on the far side of the Moon that always faces away from Earth, so you will never be able to see it. The far side, or dark side as it is often called, is covered in heavily cratered highlands (or light areas) but has very few *maria* (dark areas) when compared to the near side. The latest research suggests that when the Moon formed, the far side of the Moon cooled down quicker than the near side, which was more exposed to the heat from Earth. The quicker cooling process of the far side may have created a thicker crust on that side, meaning that when meteoroids or asteroids hit it, less volcanic lava was released.

Why do we call it the dark side of the Moon? It has nothing to do with *maria* or with actual darkness; the 'dark' reference has more to do with the 'unknown' – until humans were able to send spacecraft around the Moon, this area had never been seen…

What's in a name?

One of the most impressive Moon craters to
spot from Earth is Tycho. It is recognisable by
its bright rays that fan out, stretching 1,500km
(932mi) all around it. These rays are made
up of a mixture of rock particles that were
ejected from the blast of the meteoroid or
asteroid that hit it about 108 million years
ago. It was named after Danish astronomer
Tycho Brahe (1546–1601) who made accurate
measurements of the positions of the Sun,
Moon, planets and stars by building his
own instruments.

Shaking all over!

The Moon sometimes experiences moonquakes. These are a bit like earthquakes, but they
can last for hours rather than minutes. While earthquakes are caused by Earth's tectonic
plates moving, moonquakes are caused by the change in temperature from night to day, the
gravitational pull of Earth, or impacts from meteoroids and asteroids.

During some of the Apollo astronaut missions, seismometers (instruments that measure
and record earthquakes) were left on the Moon. Although they were switched off in 1977,
scientists have been using the data to help them study the Moon's interior. The Moon has a
thick crust on the far side (it is thinner on the near side); beneath this is the mantle (a deep
layer of denser rock); and at the centre is a small core of iron, which is partly molten (meaning
it becomes liquid when heated).

Moon
Among
Many

Our own Moon has a gravitational effect on the Earth's tides and it also keeps the tilt of our planet stable, which in turn stops our seasons from becoming too hot or too cold. But how do other moons affect their planets and what about the planets that have no moons?

Let's have a look at some of these planets and their moons, starting with those that are closest to the Sun...

Solar System

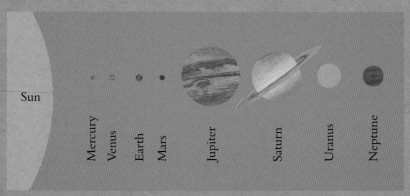

Sun

Mercury
Venus
Earth
Mars
Jupiter
Saturn
Uranus
Neptune

If Venus and Mercury had moons, they would be unlikely to affect the seasons of these planets (as our Moon does on Earth) because the temperatures on these planets are far too extreme – Mercury's temperature can reach up to 430°C (806°F); and with no atmosphere to hold in the heat, night-time temperatures can drop to -170°C (-274°F). And, despite not being closest to the Sun, Venus is the hottest planet in the solar system, with its thick atmosphere trapping heat and creating scorching temperatures of 460°C (860°F). Unlike Earth, Mercury and Venus have no seas for a moon to pull at the tides of.

Mercury

Venus

Earth

Mars

Why is it that neither Mercury nor Venus has any moons?

The Sun's gravitational pull means that Mercury wouldn't be able to hold on to a moon. Any moon that came too close to Mercury would be likely to crash into it; and any that weren't close enough would be captured by the Sun.

Scientists still don't know why Venus doesn't have a moon, but it could be for the same reasons as Mercury.

Next in line from the Sun is planet Earth and then Mars. As we know, Earth has one Moon, while Mars has two tiny moons called Phobos and Deimos. Both moons were discovered in 1877 by American astronomer Asaph Hall and are named after characters in Greek mythology.

These lumpy potato-shaped moons are smaller than most towns – with Phobos measuring 27 × 22 × 18km (17 × 14 × 11mi) and Deimos measuring just 15 × 12 × 11km (9 × 7 × 7mi).

Earth's Moon

Phobos

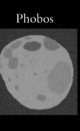

Deimos

Next are the two biggest planets in our solar system: Jupiter and Saturn. They each have more than 60 moons. Larger planets attract more moons because the bigger something is, and the closer you are to it, the greater its gravitational pull is. Once close to the planet, moons keep orbiting because gravity is strongest close to the planet, but they are moving too fast to fall down to the surface.

Jupiter

Saturn

Jupiter's four largest moons are called the Galilean moons, because they were first spotted by Galileo Galilei in 1610. They can be seen as tiny dots of light through a pair of binoculars.

Ganymede, a rocky ball of ice, is the largest moon in our solar system, measuring 5,268km (3,273mi) in diameter.

Io has over 400 erupting volcanoes and lies within Jupiter's radiation belt.

Europa, the smallest of the Galilean moons, is smooth and covered in ice, below which is believed to be a giant sea and possibly life.

Saturn has a few 'shepherd moons'. The job of these moons is to keep the planet's rings of dust and ice particles in place.

The two moons that shepherd Saturn's outer ring are called Prometheus and Pandora.

In Greek mythology, Prometheus gave humankind the gift of fire after he stole it from Mount Olympus.

Pandora was the first woman, created by the gods, as punishment for Prometheus' theft. She is said to have opened a box that released all the evils of humanity, including plagues and diseases.

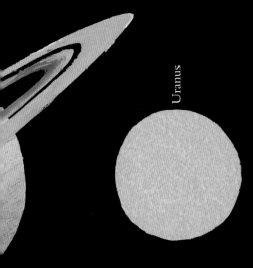

Uranus

Neptune

Uranus is believed to have 27 moons. While the first two moons, Titania and Oberon, were discovered in 1787 by British astronomer William Herschel, many of its moons were not discovered until after 1985 – either during the Voyager 2 mission in 1977 or with the help of advanced telescopes.

Titania and Oberon are Uranus's largest moons. Titania once had a huge watery ocean. As the moon cooled down at the end of its formation, it froze over and its expanding frozen interior caused the surface to crack, forming giant valleys. Oberon consists of equal amounts of rock and ice and is reddish in colour. These moons are named after characters in William Shakespeare's play *A Midsummer Night's Dream*.

Neptune has 14 moons that we know of. The first to be discovered was Triton – named after the Greek sea god. It is Neptune's largest moon and was discovered by British astronomer William Lassell in 1846, just seventeen days after the discovery of Neptune itself.

As Neptune is so far away, most of its moons were unheard of until Voyager 2 flew by the planet in 1989. Triton is the only large moon in the solar system with a retrograde orbit – it orbits in the opposite direction to Neptune's rotation – and many scientists believe that Triton formed as a planet far out in the solar system and was then captured by Neptune's gravity. It is slowly getting closer to Neptune's surface and is likely to crash into Neptune in about 3.6 billion years.

CHAPTER TWO

Heavens
Above

Gods and Goddesses

Throughout history, the Moon has often been associated with wisdom and justice. In mythology, a lunar deity is a god or goddess that represents the Moon. These lunar deities are often related to or are an enemy to solar deities (gods and goddesses of the Sun).

A religion based on ancient witchcraft traditions, known as Wicca, celebrates the cycles of the Moon. Developed in England in the first half of the 20th century, it was popularised in the 1950s by Gerald Gardner, a retired British civil servant, when he produced his spellbook, *Book of Shadows*. Wicca has now spread across the world.

Wiccans might describe their religion as having a great respect for the world around them – taking simple pleasure in watching the Sun rise or set, or in the light of the glowing Moon. They acknowledge the cycles of nature, the lunar phases and the seasons as an opportunity to celebrate their spirituality and to worship their Moon goddess or Horned god (as this religion worships both a male and female). Wiccan celebrations include ceremonies called Esbats that are held on the night of a full Moon and are dedicated to the Moon goddess.

Luna is the name of the Moon goddess in Ancient Roman mythology. The word 'lunar' came from the Latin word *luna*, meaning 'Moon'. Luna is often shown as a beautiful, pale goddess driving a chariot drawn by either two horses or two oxen (one black, and one white). In Roman art, Luna is often seen with Sol, the Ancient Roman Sun god, who drives a four-horse chariot. It is believed that Sol's chariot represents the Sun's journey through the four seasons, while Luna's chariot represents the Moon. The Ancient Romans held a yearly festival to celebrate Luna on 31st March, when there were prayers and animal sacrifices.

The Ancient Greeks' equivalent Moon goddess to Luna was Selene who happened to be the daughter of divine goddess Theia – the name given to the Mars-sized planet that is believed to have collided with Earth to form the Moon.

The Ancient Egyptians worshipped a god called Thoth. In art, he often appeared as a man with the head of an ibis (a large wading bird with a curved beak). Sometimes, he was depicted as a baboon wearing a crescent Moon on its head. Thoth had many roles in Egyptian mythology, but originally he was a Moon god. The Ancient Egyptians used the phases of the Moon to time many events in their society, including religious rituals. As a result, Thoth gradually became seen as a god of wisdom, magic and the measurement of time – and adviser to the Sun god Ra, who he stood next to on the nightly voyage across the sky.

Tsukuyomi-no-Mikoto is the Moon god in Japanese mythology and religion. It was said that there was once a god called Izanagi-no-Mikoto who created the many islands of Japan. While bathing one day, Izanagi washed Tsukuyomi out of his right eye, and the Sun goddess, Amaterasu, from his left eye and this was how Tsukuyomi and Amaterasu were born. Tsukuyomi and Amaterasu spent their lives together in the heavens. Then one day Amaterasu sent Tsukuyomi in her place to a feast held by Uke Mochi, goddess of food. Uke Mochi presented the food by throwing up from her mouth. Tsukuyomi was so disgusted that he killed her. As soon as Amaterasu heard about this, she refused to share the same part of the sky with Tsukuyomi. And this is why day and night are never together…

In Aboriginal mythology, there are tales of Bahloo the Moon man who keeps three deadly pet snakes. The Sun goddess, Yhi, was attracted to Bahloo, but he refused to notice her – and apparently this is why the Sun chases the Moon across the sky. Yhi warned the spirits who held up the sky that if they ever let Bahloo escape down to Earth, she would plunge the world into darkness.

The Hindu religion includes tales of the Moon god, Chandra. This beautiful young god carries a club and a lotus in his hands and rides his chariot across the night sky, pulled by white horses or an antelope.

In Hindu mythology, there are many legends about Chandra. In one, Chandra married the 27 daughters of Daksha, Hindu lord of creation. However, Chandra favoured one of his wives, Rohini, over the others. When they complained to Daksha he placed a curse on Chandra, causing him to lose his shine and fade away. Chandra prayed to Shiva, the creator and protector of the universe. Shiva could not reverse the curse completely but could help by bringing Chandra back for a short while.

And it is said that this is the reason why the Moon waxes and wanes.

Hanwi is the Moon goddess in Sioux mythology. The Sioux are deeply spiritual groups of Native American tribes in North America. Hanwi's name means 'Night Sun' and she is said to guard her people during the night, protecting them from evil spirits. For this reason, they pray to her – keeping moonstones nearby.

The Sioux legend tells how Hanwi's husband, the Sun god Wi, once betrayed her, allowing a beautiful mortal called Ite to sit beside him in place of Hanwi at a great feast for the gods. Skan, the sky god, was angry and so he punished Wi by taking Hanwi away from him and placing her in the night sky as the Moon. He allowed Wi to rule only the day, while Hanwi was left to rule the night, hiding her face in shame at the betrayal. It is said that this is the reason that there are Moon phases.

Chang'e is the Chinese goddess of the Moon and there are many stories about her in Chinese mythology. One such story about Chang'e is believed to be the reason that Chinese people celebrate the Mid-Autumn Moon Festival today. Long ago, it was said that ten suns rose together in the sky, scorching the earth, and making it impossible for people to grow anything. Chang'e's husband, Yi, was an archer and he shot down nine of the suns, leaving just one to give planet Earth warmth and light.

An immortal who admired Yi sent him the elixir of immortality (the gift of eternal life). But Yi's apprentice, Fengmeng, tried to steal the elixir. To stop him, Chang'e drank it herself, causing her to float up to the heavens where she then remained, living on the Moon. When Yi discovered what had happened, he felt so sad that he laid out fruits and cakes as offerings to her.

Mama Killa (meaning 'Mother Moon') is the goddess of the Moon in Inca mythology. The Incas were a South American Indian tribe that existed before the Spanish conquest began in the early 1530s. The Inca had a strange story to explain why there are dark spots on the Moon. They believed that a fox once fell in love with Mama Killa, but when it rose into the sky, she squeezed it so tightly that she produced the dark patches.

The Inca believed that lunar eclipses happened because Mama Killa was being attacked by an animal – and that such an attack could leave the world in darkness. The Inca would try to scare away this animal by throwing weapons and making noise. This tradition continued even after the Spanish invasion, which the Spanish used to their advantage. The Inca showed the Spanish great respect when they learned that the Spanish could predict an eclipse.

Gender
and
Language

Dr Charles Muses, an American philosopher and author, suggested that in many earlier religions all over the world the Moon deities tended to be male, while the Sun deities tended to be female; then somewhere along the line the male and female roles appeared to reverse. According to Charles Muses, the earlier female priests (or priestesses) honoured the Sun goddesses. But when the male priests took over they decided that as the Sun provided more light (and therefore more power), it must be male; and so the female label was often given to the Moon of lesser light.

The Moon has inspired many beliefs all over the world, throughout the centuries. But it has also helped to organise and inspire the language used for time. The name Monday comes from the Old English word *Mōnandæg* and from the Middle English word, *Monenday*, which were originally translations of the Latin phrase *dies lunae*, meaning 'day of the Moon'.

'Monday' is named after the Moon in many languages, for example, the Dutch use the word *Maandag*; the Germans use *Montag*; and the Japanese and Koreans share the same ancient Chinese words from *Hiragana* and *Hangul*, *Getsuyōbi* and *Wur-yoil*, which also mean 'day of the Moon'.

Celestial Calendars

Many religions and societies use the Moon to organise their year. This has been going on since ancient times when lunar calendars – either written down or passed on by word of mouth – helped humankind to keep a record of the best times to plant, hunt or migrate. The calendars also helped people to keep track of their religious ceremonies so that they knew when to honour their gods.

The problem with lunar calendars is that they often ignore the position of the Sun and the solar year, which is roughly 365 days long. Moon cycles of 29.5 days do not divide very easily into the year, and so they fall out of cycle every so often. In order to keep these calendars in sequence, extra days or months must be added. This is called intercalation. The UK's leap year that occurs every four years (with an extra day on 29th February) is a perfect example of this.

The traditional Chinese calendar takes into account both the Moon's phases and the Sun's movements – it is a lunisolar calendar. A year in this calendar usually has 12 months. However, about once every three years there is a leap year, which has 13 months. The earliest Chinese calendar dates back to at least the 14th century BCE – the Shang oracle bones dated around 1800–1200BCE are animal bones carved with ancient Chinese writing of the seasons and phases of the Moon.

Throughout history, many lunar calendars have included an extra month as and when needed, such as the Babylonian calendar. (Babylonia was an ancient city in Mesopotamia, now modern-day Iraq.) This calendar was also a lunisolar calendar with years usually made up of twelve lunar months (except when an extra month was added), each beginning when a new crescent Moon was first spotted on the western horizon at sunset. It was based on a much earlier calendar dating from around the 21st century BCE.

The Moon and Clocks

The Moon has influenced clockmakers too. Astronomical clocks not only tell the time, but also keep track of the positions of the Sun, Moon, stars and even some planets. The astronomical clock, or *Orloj*, in Prague in the Czech Republic, is a beautiful example. First installed in 1410, it is the third-oldest astronomical clock in the world and the oldest one still in use today. A sphere of the Moon is attached to one of the clock hands, which shows the Moon's current position as it orbits Earth. The Moon-shaped sphere even changes shape along with the actual phases of the real Moon – with a screw attached to a weight that gradually nudges and transforms the shape.

It is thought that Stonehenge – a prehistoric stone monument in Wiltshire, England – might have once been a great stone calendar. Archaeologists believe it was constructed during the years of 3000–1600BCE. Its full purpose is unknown but recent research suggests that it may have once been used as a solar calendar (similar to our 365-day calendar) as well as a lunar calendar.

This would have helped ancient societies to know when to farm around the seasons. Stone markers used alongside holes dug around the monument are believed to have been a way of tracking each passing day as well as the Moon's phases – and possibly even of predicting eclipses.

The traditional Chinese calendar starts its year between late January and early February and is used by the Chinese community to work out when important festivals, such as Chinese New Year, will happen. But did you know that there is a festival dedicated to the Moon, which takes place every autumn? The Mid-Autumn Moon Festival is a harvest festival celebrated by Chinese and Vietnamese people. It takes place on the fifteenth day of the eighth month of the lunar calendar when the Moon is full.

The festival was originally a time to enjoy a successful harvest of rice and wheat, and food was offered to the Moon. It has been celebrated since the Shang dynasty around 1600–1046BCE.

The ancient Chinese associated the Moon with rejuvenation. An old fable told that the Sun and the Moon had stars as their children. When the Moon was pregnant it became round, and once it had given birth it became a crescent. This belief led many Chinese women to worship the Moon during the festival.

Today, Chinese friends and families gather together to give thanks for what they have and to pray for good fortune. The celebrations might involve watching the Moon, while lighting paper lanterns and eating mooncakes – pastry cases filled with a sweet filling and salted egg yolks that symbolise the full Moon.

Food offerings are also made to the Moon goddess, Chang'e, on 15th August as this is the date she is said to have drunk the elixir of immortality.

Buddhism, the main religion in many Asian countries, follows a lunar calendar too. The practice of Buddhism focuses on personal spiritual development. It follows in the path of Buddha, Siddhārtha Gautama, who went on a quest for enlightenment at some point between the 6th and 4th centuries BCE.

Buddhism's most important festival, Wesak, or Buddha Day, celebrates the birth, enlightenment and death of Siddhārtha Gautama. It takes place every May on the night of the full Moon as it is believed that this is when all three of these events occurred. Wesak is a time when Buddhists visit temples or monasteries to listen to stories about Siddhārtha Gautama's life. They often repeat mantras and meditate, and give each other cards and presents.

Easter Sunday is the Christian celebration of Jesus Christ's Resurrection, when he rose from the dead. In Western Christianity, Easter is the first Sunday after the paschal full Moon, which is said to be the first full Moon on or after 21st March. As the paschal full Moon, or fourteenth day of a lunar month, doesn't always land on the same day each year, it can mean that Easter might fall any time between 22nd March and 25th April.

The Islamic year also follows the lunar calendar, which is why the month of Ramadan, a period of prayer and fasting, starts at a different time of the year each year. Muslims wait for sightings of the first crescent of a new Moon before they know what day it will begin. It usually ends when the first crescent of the new Moon is sighted again.

Symbols and Signs

While the real Moon overlooks us from above Earth, symbols of the Moon have crept into our everyday lives down on Earth…

Flag of Pakistan

The crescent Moon and star is a well-known symbol of Islam that's recognised around the world. It can be seen on many flags of Muslim countries, such as Pakistan and Algeria. It is believed that the crescent Moon and star symbol was actually in use before the religion of Islam by several thousand years – by the people of central Asia and Siberia in their worship of the Sun, Moon and sky gods.

Flag of Algeria

It wasn't until the Ottoman (or Turkish) Empire that the crescent Moon and star became linked with the Muslim world. When the Turks conquered the city of Constantinople (modern-day Istanbul) in 1453, they adopted the city's existing flag and symbol. And for hundreds of years, the Ottoman Empire ruled over the Muslim world so it's easy to see how this symbol eventually crept in…

Hot cross buns are traditionally eaten on Good Friday (the Friday before Easter Sunday). It's often thought that the cross on the bun represents the cross that Jesus died upon, but in fact the hot cross bun can be traced back much further...

It is believed that buns originated with the Assyrians and Babylonians as they worshipped their gods and goddesses. Many other cultures offered cakes to their own Moon gods and goddesses. The Egyptians gave cakes decorated with bull's horns, symbolic of the crescent Moon; the Ancient Greeks replaced the horns with a cross symbolising the Moon's four quarters; while the Romans ate these cakes in honour of their own lunar goddess. The Easter connection is said to come from the Anglo-Saxons who gave crossed buns as an offering to their goddess Eostre, the goddess of spring.

In the Chinese yin and yang symbol, the yin part of the symbol (black side with white dot) is often associated with the dark and cold; while the yang part (white side with black dot) is often associated with heat and light.

In Chinese philosophy, the yin and yang symbol is used to make us aware of how we are feeling, so that we can make the changes necessary in order to make us feel more balanced – for example, if we are too cold, then we must take steps to make ourselves warmer.

THE MOON

Most traditional tarot (fortune-telling) cards contain a Moon card – the card of intuition, dreams and the unconscious. This card tells a story of the crayfish or lobster (supposedly the person who is having their fortune told) that crawls out of the water (representing our subconscious) to go on an important journey through the darkest night.

The light of the Moon, representing clear thinking, guides the way past distractions and challenges – a dog, yapping at us to 'do the right thing' and a wolf, howling at us to 'go wild' – and on to our highest goals.

While it is believed that ancient stone monuments were built to track the movements of the Sun and Moon (as well as being places of worship), the Nebra sky disc was more of a portable tool. The 30cm (12in) bronze disc – with its gold symbols of the Sun, Moon and stars – is said to be one of the most important archaeological finds of the 20th century because it shows the most accurate picture of the night sky in ancient history. The disc, dating back to 1600BCE, was found in Nebra, Germany, in an area containing around 1,000 burial mounds. It is believed to have come from the Bronze Age and is so valuable that it was once circulating on the illegal market with a price tag of a quarter of a million pounds!

Moon Signs

While you might be familiar with star signs, did you know that many cultures throughout history had Moon signs, for example, the Chinese and Old English? Native American tribes often gave names to each full Moon throughout the year in order to keep track of the seasons.

January: the Wolf Moon

The Wolf Moon appeared in January when snow gathered deep in the woods and hungry wolves howled outside the villages. Some tribes called this the Snow Moon, but that was mainly used as the name for February's full Moon.

February: the Snow Moon

This tended to be the year's snowiest month, hence the name of the full Moon. Among tribes that used this name for the January Moon, the February Moon was called the Hunger Moon because of the challenging hunting conditions.

March: the Worm Moon

As the snow began to melt, earthworms began to show their heads again. Early signs of spring led to other names for this Moon: the cawing of crows (the Crow Moon); the formation of crusts on the snow as it thawed and froze again (the Crust Moon); and the time for tapping maple trees (the Sap Moon).

April: the Pink Moon

Many pink flowers began to bloom and a carpet of new grass began to grow. Other names for this Moon, such as the Sprouting Grass Moon and Egg Moon, were inspired by signs of spring.

May: the Flower Moon

More flowers came into bloom and the corn was ready to plant – while cows, goats and sheep enjoyed grazing on the pastures, producing lots of rich milk. This was also called the Corn Planting Moon and the Milk Moon.

June: the Strawberry Moon

This was the start of the strawberry-picking season. It is one of the few names that was used by all Algonquin tribes.

The best-known names came from the Algonquin tribes who lived in the area of New England and westward to Lake Superior (the largest Great Lake of North America). The Europeans who settled in North America continued to use many of the names. A variety of different ones were used, but here are the most common…

July: the Buck Moon

The bucks (male deer) began to grow new antlers after shedding them the previous year. The summer storms in New England also led to the name Thunder Moon, while some tribes used Hay Moon, after the July hay harvest.

August: the Sturgeon Moon

Named after the sturgeon – a large fish that was often caught in the Great Lakes in this month. This full Moon was also called the Red Moon because of its colour as it rose in the hazy August skies, or the Green Corn Moon or Grain Moon, as it sometimes came at the time of the corn harvest.

September: the Harvest Moon

Many of the tribes' main foods, such as corn, pumpkins, beans and rice were ready for gathering at this time. The strong light of the Harvest Moon allowed European farmers to work late into the night to harvest their crops. Sometimes this Moon was also called the Corn Moon.

October: the Hunter's Moon

After the fields had been reaped, the leaves began to fall and plenty of fattened deer roamed the lands. Under the light of this Moon, hunters could spot these animals more easily.

November: the Beaver Moon

Some say the name of this full Moon came about because the Native Americans set beaver traps around this time – in order to have warm winter furs. Others say it's just because the beavers were busy building their winter dams in this month.

December: the Cold Moon

This full Moon was named after the freezing temperatures of winter. It was sometimes called the Long Night Moon as the winter nights lengthened and the Moon spent a longer time above the horizon. The name often used by Christian settlers was the 'Moon before Yule', meaning 'Moon before Christmas'.

CHAPTER THREE

Mysterious Moon Myths

Man in the Moon

In western parts of the Northern Hemisphere, people often think they can see parts of a face, head or body on the Moon. What they are actually seeing are the *maria*, or volcanic 'seas' (the dark areas) and the highlands or mountains (the light areas) on the Moon's surface.

Christian tradition tells of a man who carries sticks on his back, who is sent to live on the Moon for eternity after committing a crime. The tale is said to be inspired by a tale in the King James Bible. In the story, the children of Israel stumble upon a man who is gathering sticks on the Sabbath Day. As this is supposed to be a 'day of rest', God punishes him by sentencing him to death.

A similar tale exists in Germany – about an old man who gathers a bundle of sticks on a Sunday. He meets a stranger who states that, as he doesn't value his Sunday on Earth, he must spend an endless 'Moon-day' in heaven – as a warning to all Sabbath-breakers. He is given the choice of either burning in the Sun or of freezing on the Moon, but he chooses the latter. Supposedly you can now spot the old man carrying sticks during a full Moon.

In Haida mythology, the figure is a boy gathering sticks. (The Haida are the Native American people living on the Pacific coast of Canada.) In the story, the boy's father tells him that the Moon will provide light to help with the search for sticks. But the lazy boy refuses to do the work and instead teases the Moon. As punishment, the boy is taken from Earth and trapped on the Moon.

The people of Rantum – a small village on the German island of Sylt – say the Man in the Moon is a giant who controls the Earth's tides, pouring water onto Earth to create high tides, and taking a rest as the waters die down.

Another old German tale tells of a woman who makes butter on the Sabbath Day – she is banished to the Moon and is said to still be up there, holding a butter tub.

In Scandinavian mythology of the 13th century, the Moon (known as Máni) steals two children – a boy and a girl (Hjúki and Bil) from their parents. They are drawing water from a well at the time of capture – and it is said that you can see the children on the Moon, carrying a pail of water between them.

The Moon Rabbit

While some parts of the world can see the Man in the Moon, many people in the East, or Asia, and some of the Americas believe they can see a rabbit, or hare. Again this has inspired many stories over the centuries, particularly among the Chinese community and the Native Americans.

According to Chinese legend, the Moon Rabbit is a good friend of the Moon goddess Chang'e and pounds the elixir of life for her in its mortar. It is said to live in the Moon with a toad and can be seen every year on 15th August during the Mid-Autumn Moon Festival.

The Moon Rabbit is also popular in Japan and Korea. In their versions of the story, the rabbit pounds the ingredients for rice cakes in its bowl rather than the elixir of life.

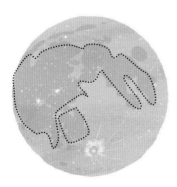

Japan and Korea also celebrate the Mid-Autumn Moon Festival. As in China, people gather to watch the full Moon and children sing a song about the Moon Rabbit.

A number of Native Americans in the United States, Canada and Mexico also have stories about the Moon Rabbit. The Aztecs believed that the god Quetzalcoatl lived on Earth as a man at one time. One story describes a great journey that Quetzalcoatl goes on, when he runs out of food. The Moon Rabbit finds him and offers itself as a meal in order to save his life. Humbled by the rabbit's offer, Quetzalcoatl takes the rabbit to the Moon and brings it back to Earth. He tells the rabbit that it will be remembered by all as its image is now in the light of the Moon.

In African mythology, there is a tale about the Moon and a hare, rather than a rabbit. In the story, the Moon wishes to send a message to the humans on Earth: that just as she 'dies' and lives again, so they too will die and live again. But the hare gets its words mixed up, dooming all of the people to be mortal (to eventually die) instead.

The Cree, one of the largest groups of
First Nations in North America, has a
story about a rabbit that wishes to ride
to the Moon, but only the crane is willing to
take it. During the flight, the large rabbit holds
on to the crane's legs, stretching them in the
process – and it's said that is why the crane has
such long legs today. In the story, the rabbit also
touches the crane's head with a bloody paw,
rewarding it with the red markings that the
crane has today.

A Shady Character...

While the Moon has been a source of comfort for many among the human race, others have been superstitious of it and have even linked it with death…

Misreading the Signs?

Archaeologists investigating the Middle-Stone-Age site of Pinnacle Point, a small headland on the coast of South Africa, think that modern humans set up 'home' on the coast because it was too difficult to survive in the dry inland. They lived on shellfish that came in with the spring tides, and may have studied the Moon's phases so they knew when the low spring tides would be. Those that misread the lunar phases and went out at high tide are likely to have drowned…

Light and Darkness

In Hindu culture, death is associated with the loss of consciousness and is symbolised by darkness. The Sun is a source of light and has become a symbol for God, while the Moon has become a symbol for the cycle of birth and death as it regularly moves between light and darkness.

Lost Souls

Early Hindus even believed that the souls of the dead returned to the Moon for rebirth. The Bhagavad Gita (a collection of sacred Hindu writings, from around the 5th to the 2nd century BCE) describes two paths that souls travel along after death. One is the path of the Sun (on which a soul never returns), and the other is the path of the Moon (on which a soul does return).

Maneater

The Maori people believed the Moon was the cause of death and called it 'Hina the maneater', while the early Tatars (Turkic-speaking people of Russia and other parts of central Asia and Europe) are said to have believed that a man-devouring giant lived in the Moon!

... Or a Victim?

While some superstitions and myths have shown the Moon in a villainous light, others have shown it to be more of a victim…

The Efik Ibibio people (one of the largest groups living in Nigeria, West Africa) have a myth involving a flood. When the Sun and Moon (who happen to be husband and wife) invite their friend Flood to pay them a visit on Earth, Flood declines the offer – saying their house is too small.

So the Sun and Moon build a house the size of a palace and invite Flood once again. When Flood at last agrees to visit, he rises quickly to the rafters and the Sun and Moon are forced onto their house roof. As Flood continues to rise over the top of the house, the poor Sun and Moon have to leap into the sky…

A myth belonging to the native people of central and
southern Africa tells of the Sun and Moon belonging
to a clan. One day as children, they go to herd cattle
but they cannot agree on whose cattle should drink
from the stream first. They begin to argue and wrestle
with each other. The Moon throws the Sun into the
mud and the Sun then retaliates by throwing the
Moon into the mud.

The Sun says that they are now even and asks the
Moon to wash him. The Moon does so and makes
the Sun bright and shiny again; but the Sun refuses to
wash the Moon in turn. It is said that the dull Moon
is so ashamed of her appearance that she now hides
during the daytime and only comes out at night.

The Fox and the Wolf

A fable

There was once a greedy wolf who lived in a forest. One night he came across a fox and eyed her hungrily. But the wily fox had a plan, and said to the wolf: "Follow me, and you will have as much to eat as you want." The fox led the wolf to a lake and pointed to the reflection of the Moon. "Just look at that tasty wheel of cheese!" The wolf licked his lips, and began lapping at the water. He drank more and more water and became fatter and fatter until finally – pop! – the wolf burst into a million pieces!

CHAPTER FOUR

The
Moon
and
our
Bodies

Body
of
Influence

Did you know that over half of your body weight is made up of water? Even your bones contain water!

Can the Moon cause tides to rise and fall inside our bodies?

We know that the Moon and Sun can both cause a gravitational pull on the Earth's tides. This gravitational pull is so strong that even our planet's crust can be stretched by it. This 'stretching' is known as an Earth tide.

Ocean tides happen because both the Moon and Earth have a large mass, creating a huge attraction between the two.

Our planet has two high tides and two low tides a day, which occur on opposite sides of the Earth. However, no one has found any evidence that the Moon's gravitational pull affects the water on the opposite sides of our bodies. Might it be that the 'tides' are just too small to detect? After all, some lakes have tides – they are just too small for you to notice…

Women and Fertility

Many people believe that the Moon can affect when a woman is likely to become pregnant. Throughout history a lot of cultures have linked the cycle of the Moon with women's fertility. It's called the lunar effect – changes in the body and behaviour of living beings according to the different phases of the Moon.

So is there any truth behind the idea that the Moon and its phases might affect a woman's fertility? There haven't been many studies on this – most of the available information is based on women's personal experiences. But the idea that a woman can become pregnant more easily during a full Moon has been around for centuries.

The Ancient Romans believed this, which is why their goddess of fertility was also the goddess of the Moon. (Diana was the Roman goddess of the hunt and wild animals. She later took over from Luna as the Roman goddess of the Moon, responsible for fertility and childbirth.)

Are more babies born at the time of a full Moon?

You may have heard it said that a higher number of babies are born on the night of a full Moon. However, over the years, researchers have come up with little evidence that this is the case.

In fact, a 2001 study carried out by astronomer and physicist Daniel Caton, using 20 years' worth of data from the USA's National Center for Health Statistics, found no correlation between the full Moon and births. And this was after analysing 70 million deliveries!

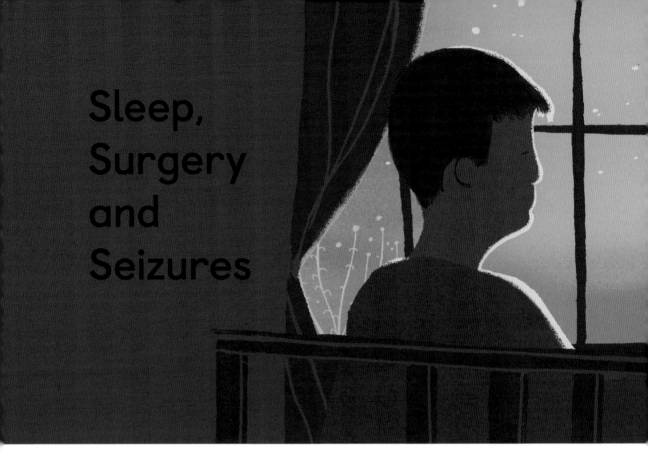

Sleep,
Surgery
and
Seizures

A study carried out at the University of Basel in Switzerland in 2000 suggests that the Moon may affect our sleep…

The study involved 33 people sleeping in a completely dark laboratory. Recordings were made over three and a half days, and none of the 'sleepers' knew that the Moon's phases might be a factor in the data collection. The study showed that people got 20 minutes less sleep during the full Moon.

It also took them five more minutes to fall asleep, and they experienced 30 per cent less deep sleep than they did on nights without a full Moon.

So could a full Moon really reduce the quality of our sleep?

It seems possible, doesn't it? Interestingly, research has suggested that the lunar effect on sleep might, in fact, be related to the increased amount of light that shines down on us before we go to sleep on the night of a full Moon.

But if it *is* possible for the full Moon to affect activities like sleep, could it also affect other situations – such as the success of surgery? It is sometimes claimed that surgeons used to refuse to operate during the full Moon. They believed that patients lost more blood around this time, increasing the risk of death…

However...

In 2013 the Interactive Cardiovascular and Thoracic Surgery journal published an article about a study that took place at Rhode Island Hospital in the United States. Researchers found that patients who had emergency heart surgery during a waning full Moon were *less* likely to die; and those that had surgery during a full Moon were likely to spend four days less time in hospital than patients who had the same operation during other Moon phases.

While no one is in agreement about whether a full Moon is related to the outcome of surgery, some believe that the Moon might be linked to epileptic seizures, where the body 'fits' and shakes uncontrollably. Society once blamed epilepsy on witchcraft or demonic possession as, without any medical knowledge, humans sought a 'mystical' explanation for this condition.

But is there any truth in it?

In the late 2000s a study was carried out by the Institute of Neurology at the University College London. Researchers examined the records that were kept by an epilepsy unit, in which the time of their patients' seizures was logged.

The study showed that the number of epileptic seizures was *fewer* when the Moon was at its brightest. Experts have suggested that melatonin, a hormone that the body only releases at night and in the dark, may be the real cause of such seizures.

CHAPTER **FIVE**

The
Moon
and
our
Behaviour

A
Crazy
Phase

The word 'lunacy' and the idea of being 'moonstruck' describe situations when people might be acting strangely… In fact the word 'lunatic' came from the Latin word *luna* (meaning 'Moon') – based on the belief that changes in the Moon caused moments of insanity.

So has anyone studied a connection between the phases of the Moon and our behaviour?

Guy Cramer, president of the aerospace science company United Dynamics Corp, in Colorado, USA, has researched this. He's suggested that the full Moon might have influenced voters' behaviour in the 2000 US Presidential Election. But how? He believes in the idea that positive and negative ions (molecules in the atmosphere, which have a positive or negative charge) are directly linked with the Moon; and that the number of positive ions increases around the time of a full Moon.

When comparing data for the number of positive and negative ions in the atmosphere alongside people's opinions about the election candidates, Guy Cramer noticed something in the four weeks leading up to the 7th November election…

On days of high *negative* ion activity, the voting public tended to lean more towards candidate George W. Bush (who went on to become 43rd President of the United States). According to Guy Cramer, these were days when people were calm and thinking clearly. On days of high *positive* ion activity around the time of the full Moon, when people were apparently more stressed and feeling 'out of sorts', they were supportive of the opposition, Al Gore.

It is Guy Cramer's belief that the full Moon increases the high number of positive ions in the atmosphere, which can occur alongside the unusual or 'disturbed' behaviour of people during these times. Supporters of Al Gore may, of course, disagree as to which group of people was 'thinking clearly'…

So how might a full Moon affect people's outlook on life? Would they be less willing to take a risk on something like the stock exchange during a full Moon phase, meaning that profits on investments wouldn't be so high?

Ilia D. Dichev and Troy D. Janes, both of the University of Michigan Business School in the United States, seem to think so. Their study of more than 20 stock exchanges over 30 years shows a strong link between lunar cycles and stock prices.

A chart published in the *Journal of Private Equity* in 2003 showed the daily profits on the stock exchange for several G-7 countries (countries that represent more than 64 per cent of our overall global wealth), such as the United States, the United Kingdom and Japan. The profits were higher around the new Moon than the full Moon.

People who work in the emergency services, such as police, doctors and nurses, have often said that they are busier on nights of a full Moon. So do more emergency situations occur on these nights? Many studies have been carried out, yet there is no solid evidence to support this.

Maybe it's all to do with statistics, rather than lunacy. A beautiful full Moon might attract more people to go out on such nights – or the extra light provided by a full Moon might help criminals to carry out their acts. Who knows? But if there is even slightly more activity on a full Moon night, then that may result in a minor increase in crime, accidents and injuries.

It might be that the light of a full Moon keeps people awake – and the less sleep that people have, the less likely they are to make sensible decisions. Or perhaps when strange things happen, people notice the full Moon; but when strange things happen during other Moon phases they don't pay any attention to the night sky.

Behaving Like Animals

It's not just human behaviour that might be affected by the Moon's phases. Studies suggest that more pets are taken into veterinary emergency rooms during the full Moon, so does this mean that animals are acting strangely on these nights too?

For some animals, the full Moon means new beginnings… and this can be seen along Australia's Great Barrier Reef once every year. Each Australian spring, thousands of corals release their eggs and sperm into the water, making it look like a multi-coloured snowstorm!

Scientists say that the corals can tell when the Moon is full, thanks to an ancient gene that helps them to sense how much moonlight is hitting the water. All different types of Australian corals use the lunar cycle to release their eggs and sperm at around the same time, making reproduction much more successful.

Just northwest of Australia lies Christmas Island, where another watery union takes place…

At the same time each year during the wet season, millions of red crabs (*Gecarcoidea natalis*) journey from the forest to the coast to breed and release their eggs into the sea. And the timing of their journey is linked to the Moon's phases. It's important that the female crabs release their eggs into the sea at the high tide during the last quarter of the Moon. This is the time of the neap tides (when there is the least difference between high and low tides), so it is safer for the females approaching the water's edge to release their eggs. It also means that the larvae (young crabs) will not drift too far from the island.

The reproductive cycles of many marine animals are linked to changing levels of moonlight and the tides, both of which are affected by the Moon's phases. Animals that time their behaviour with the lunar cycle are said to have a circalunar clock.

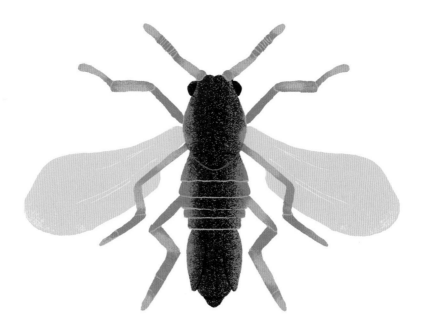

The non-biting midge (*Clunio marinus*) lives in the intertidal zone of the European Atlantic Coast (an area that is above water at low tide and under water at high tide). The adult midges only live for a few hours and so, during this time, they must reproduce. They do so only during the lowest of low tides, which occur during the spring tides around both the new and full Moon.

To time this just right, the midges have two internal clocks: a circadian (daily) clock, which is set by the Sun; and the circalunar (monthly) clock, which is set by the Moon. But, the times of the lowest of low tides are different, depending on the location. So the midges have to 'set' their clocks according to where they are at the time. Research suggests that a protein inside the creature might keep the clocks in line with what is going on in the environment.

Samoan palolo worms (*Palola viridis*) live in the waters of the Pacific islands around Samoa, northeast of Australia, and only reproduce during the last quarter of the Moon. For a few nights during spring or early summer, tens of thousands of these worms lose their rear ends!

Palolo worms spend most of their lives burrowing in shallow water. Before spawning, they begin to grow tails, which contain either sperm or eggs (depending on whether the worms are male or female). These 'tails' also have 'eyespots' (small areas which can detect moonlight).

When the Moon phase is just right, the worms release these tails, which rise to the water's surface. Meanwhile, the rest of the worms' bodies remain attached to the ocean floor. They grow new tails each year for the yearly spawn.

The worms' tails, or epitokes as they are known, are a delicacy (a rare treat) for the local people and are eaten boiled, fried or raw. But humans have to be quick to catch them before they dissolve into a mixture of eggs and sperm, which soon develop into larvae and drift down to the ocean floor to become adult worms.

Widely distributed in the rock coral of the West Indies is the Atlantic palolo (*E. furcata, or E. schemocephala*), which swarms during the last quarter of the June–July Moon. The Japanese palolo (*Tylorrhynchus heterochaetus*), also considered a culinary delicacy, lives in the coastal waters of Japan.

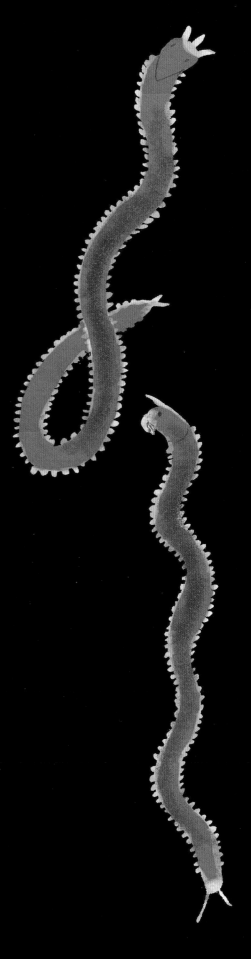

It's not all about reproduction by the sea. Some animal species use the phases of the Moon to help guide them towards food, or prey…

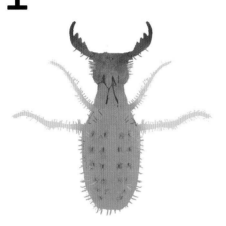

The larvae of antlions (*Myrmeleontidae*, dragonfly-like insects) are famous for digging holes in sand to catch other insect prey, such as ants or spiders. But under the light of a full Moon they dig even bigger holes. It's believed that insects are more active in the moonlight, so these larger holes might increase the antlions' chances of catching more victims.

From one lion to another… African lions (*Panthera leo*) usually hunt best at night. However, they will sometimes make a kill during the day, especially after a full Moon. This is because they tend to eat less food during moonlit nights (when their prey is less active and harder to catch); and so might go on a hunting frenzy during the days and nights that follow a full Moon.

Some species of nightjar (*Caprimulgidae*, birds that come out at night) will lay their eggs in phase with the lunar cycle, so that they hatch around ten days before a full Moon. Because of this, when the Moon is nearly full and at its brightest, the adults can hunt large amounts of insects at night to feed to their chicks.

While some animals use the Moon's light to their advantage, others hide away from it. This fear of the Moon is called 'lunar phobia' and apparently many bats all over the world are scared into the shadows when the Moon comes out.

Scientists in Mexico discovered that most of the bats living and foraging in open spaces were less 'active' during moonlit nights than those living in darker, sheltered areas. This could be because bats are more easily spotted by predators in open areas when the Moon is bright. Studies also show that some of the bats who spent most of their time above the treetops were no less active on well-lit nights – possibly because they were a faster-flying species that lived among fewer predators.

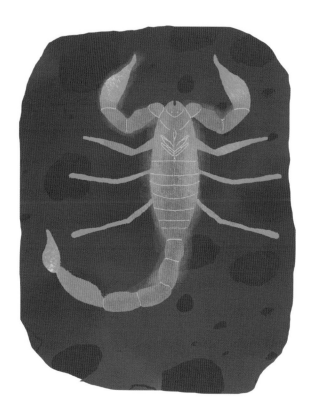

Did you know that scorpions can glow in the dark? This happens when ultraviolet (UV) rays of moonlight react with a substance in their outer skeletons. Some researchers think this might help scorpions to find each other in the desert; others think it's used to dazzle prey. Further studies have suggested that scorpions use their glow-in-the-dark technique to help them decide if it's safe to leave their burrows in search of food.

Scorpions are nocturnal creatures, but they dislike coming out on moonlit nights, especially at full Moon. It's believed that while they can't detect moonlight – and so wouldn't know if a bright night allowed predators to see them – they can see 'green' and so are able to detect their own glow under the Moon.

CHAPTER SIX

Moon Imagination

From the Page...

The Moon has been the subject of many works of art and literature, and has inspired many people from authors to songwriters, and poets to film-makers. It's no wonder that many sleepless writers might have looked to the Moon for a moment of revelation.

Telling Tales

One of the earliest fictional writings about the Moon was a famous poem written by Italian poet Ludovico Ariosto and published in 1532. The extremely long poem, *Orlando Furioso* (The Frenzy of Orlando), has 38,736 lines in total, making it one of the longest in European literature. It tells the tale of a knight, Orlando, who falls in love with Princess Angelica. But when Angelica falls in love with someone else, Orlando goes mad, destroying everything in his path.

To help Orlando, another knight, Astolfo, flies to the Moon in a flaming chariot. In the poem, everything lost on Earth can be found on the Moon – including Orlando's senses. So Astolfo brings them back in a bottle and when he makes Orlando sniff the contents, he makes him sane again.

With the invention of the telescope in the early 1600s, people became aware that our Moon might not be quite as smooth and 'perfect' as it seemed from a distance... It now appeared to be another Earth-like sphere, with mountains and craters. This may have inspired writers to think that other life might exist up there...

German mathematician and astronomer Johannes Kepler, who developed his own telescope in 1611, wrote a novel called *Somnium* in 1608. The title is Latin for 'The Dream' and is about an Icelandic boy and his witch mother. His mother is able to summon demons that tell them about far away places, one of which is an island named Levania (our Moon). The book includes a detailed description of how Earth might look from the Moon, and is thought to have been one of the first science-fiction books to look at the Moon in a realistic way.

More Moon Stories

Jules Verne was a French writer. His book *De la Terre à la Lune* (From the Earth to the Moon), published in 1865, was the first science-fiction novel about travelling to the Moon. It is about a group of weapons enthusiasts who build an enormous cannon, in which they hope to send three people to the Moon. Verne even included some calculations on the cannon's design, influenced by some of the technologies of the time.

Jules Verne's sequel *Autour de la Lune* (Around the Moon), published in 1870, goes on to explain what happens to the three men on their journey to the Moon.

English author H.G. Wells took the idea of Moon adventures even further in his 1901 story *The First Men in the Moon*. In his novel, businessman Mr Bedford and scientist Mr Cavor travel to the Moon in a spaceship. When they land on the Moon, the men discover insect-like creatures called 'Selenites' living inside it (the creatures are named after the Ancient Greek Moon goddess Selene).

Travel to the Moon and beyond had caught the public's imagination and became an even more popular theme in the media, including children's stories…

The Adventures of Tintin comics by Belgian cartoonist Georges Remi (who wrote under the name Hergé) took children on a journey to the Moon. The adventure series began as a comic strip in a children's Belgian newspaper supplement, *Le Petit Vingtième* (The Little Twentieth), in 1929.

Tintin, a young reporter and adventurer, is the hero of the stories, helped by his loyal dog Snowy. In *Objectif Lune* (Destination Moon) published as a collection in 1953, Tintin and his friend Captain Haddock get an invitation from Professor Calculus to visit the fictional country of Syldavia, where the professor is working on a top-secret project: a manned mission to the Moon.

Before writing the *Tintin* adventures, Hergé carried out a lot of research into the possibility of human space travel. He wanted his stories to be as realistic as possible. His Moon rocket was inspired by the design of the V-2 rocket developed by the Germans during World War II, and his idea of a spacesuit came very close to the one used in future Moon exploration…

You Will Go to the Moon, written by Mae and Ira Freeman, was first published in the United States in 1959 – ten years before the first Moon landing. The tale about a young boy taking an imaginary trip to the Moon became part of the *Beginner Books* series to help young readers, as supervised by popular American children's writer, Dr Seuss (Theodor Giesel).

In the lead-up to the Apollo Moon landings, this was one of the first books to inspire young children about the reality of travelling to the Moon. It explained in a simple way how the mission would work, while trying to keep the science behind it all very real – including the launch of a three-stage rocket.

The authors and editors were so concerned to get the scientific points as accurate as possible that they asked the Office of the Director of Research and Development of the United States Air Force to check it.

Then in 1961, US President John F. Kennedy announced that America would land astronauts on the Moon before 1970, and the fantasy started to become reality…

The *Matthew Looney* series of children's books by American author Jerome Beatty Jr (written 1961–1978) is a set of space stories about a 'non-human' boy. Matthew and his sister Maria live in the town of Crater Plato on the Moon, whose inhabitants are determined to invade Earth. The series was written at the height of the Space Race, when children were captivated by the idea of space missions and adventures to the Moon.

Even today – fifty years since the first Moon landing – the subject still inspires authors the world over…

Maggot Moon written by British author Sally Gardner in 2012 is set in 1950s England, imagining what life could have been like if the Allies – Britain, France, Italy, Russia and the United States – had lost World War II. Standish Treadwell, 15, is dyslexic and very aware of what's going on around him. He and his friend Hector dream of reaching the stars as the Motherland plots to be the first nation to land a man on the Moon. But the Motherland's Moon launch is not quite as it appears…

Fire!

*T*he moon advanced upward in a heaven of the purest clearness, outshining in her passage the twinkling light of the stars. She passed over the constellation of the Twins, and was now nearing the halfway point between the horizon and the zenith. A terrible silence weighed upon the entire scene! Not a breath of wind upon the earth! Not a sound of breathing from the countless chests of the spectators! Their hearts seemed afraid to beat! All eyes were fixed upon the yawning mouth of the Columbiad.*

Murchison followed with his eye the hand of his chronometer. It wanted scarce forty seconds to the moment of departure, but each second seemed to last an age! At the twentieth there was a general shudder, as it occurred to the minds of that vast assemblage that the bold travellers shut up within the projectile were also counting those terrible seconds. Some few cries here and there escaped the crowd.

"Thirty-five! — thirty-six! — thirty-seven! — thirty-eight! — thirty-nine! — forty! FIRE!!!"

Instantly Murchison pressed with his finger the key of the electric battery, restored the current of the fluid, and discharged the spark into the breech of the Columbiad.

An appalling unearthly report followed instantly, such as can be compared to nothing whatever known, not even to the roar of thunder, or the blast of volcanic explosions! No words can convey the slightest idea of the terrific sound!

An immense spout of fire shot up from the bowels of the earth as from a crater. The earth heaved up, and with great difficulty some few spectators obtained a momentary glimpse of the projectile victoriously cleaving the air in the midst of the fiery vapours!

Extract from *De la Terre à la Lune* by Jules Verne

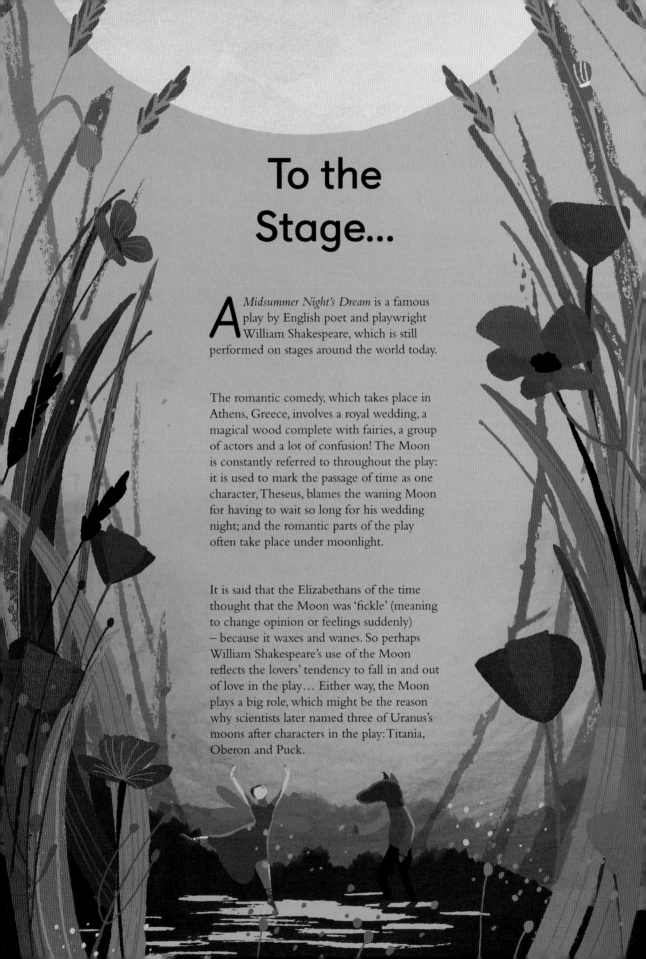

To the Stage...

A *Midsummer Night's Dream* is a famous play by English poet and playwright William Shakespeare, which is still performed on stages around the world today.

The romantic comedy, which takes place in Athens, Greece, involves a royal wedding, a magical wood complete with fairies, a group of actors and a lot of confusion! The Moon is constantly referred to throughout the play: it is used to mark the passage of time as one character, Theseus, blames the waning Moon for having to wait so long for his wedding night; and the romantic parts of the play often take place under moonlight.

It is said that the Elizabethans of the time thought that the Moon was 'fickle' (meaning to change opinion or feelings suddenly) – because it waxes and wanes. So perhaps William Shakespeare's use of the Moon reflects the lovers' tendency to fall in and out of love in the play… Either way, the Moon plays a big role, which might be the reason why scientists later named three of Uranus's moons after characters in the play: Titania, Oberon and Puck.

To the Big Screen...

The first film about travelling to the Moon was a French silent movie made in 1902, directed by Georges Méliès. *Le Voyage dans la Lune* (A Trip to the Moon), which showed a rocket landing in the Moon's eye, was inspired by the novels of Jules Verne and *The First Men in the Moon* by H.G. Wells. The film is about a group of astronomers who fly to the Moon in a capsule, escape from the Selenites living underground, and return to Earth with one of them captive. It was not meant to be realistic, but poked fun at the science of the time.

One of the first science-fiction silent movies to be taken seriously was *Frau im Mond*, released in Germany in 1929. Directed by Fritz Lang, the film was released in the United States as *By Rocket to the Moon*, and in the United Kingdom as *Woman in the Moon*. The basics of rocket travel were seen by a large audience for the first time, including a multi-stage rocket. The film and its rocket design were taken so seriously that the Nazis banned it until 1945, because of how similar it was to their secret V-2 project.

The cartoon rabbit Bugs Bunny was ahead of the times! He became the first rabbit to fly to the Moon in Warner Brothers' 1948 cartoon *Haredevil Hare*. Poor Bugs Bunny is dragged onto a rocket against his will – but soon cheers up when he sees that it's full of carrots! And once up on the Moon, he stops Marvin the Martian from blowing up Earth.

Destination Moon (released in 1950), produced by George Pal and directed by Irving Pichel, was the first major US science-fiction film to deal with the dangers of human space travel. In the final scene, as the crew approaches Earth, instead of 'The End' scrolling across the screen, the words: 'This is THE END... of the Beginning' are shown, signalling what was to come...

Walt Disney's three-part television series *Man in Space*, *Man and the Moon* and *Mars and Beyond* was broadcast between 1955 and 1957. Using a combination of documentary footage and animation, the shows included the history of rockets, a humorous look at our fascination with the Moon, and actors reconstructing 'live-action' scenes inside a specially designed Moon rocket ship: Lunar Reconn Ship RM-1.

Walt Disney's studio worked closely with German engineer Wernher von Braun (inventor of the V-2 rocket), who helped advise the studio on technical information. By reaching such a large audience, Disney helped to make many see that the Moon landing might no longer be the stuff of science fiction... Wernher von Braun oversaw most of the US space programme including the 1969 Moon landing.

Apollo 13, the 1995 American film starring Tom Hanks, was based on the real events of the seventh manned mission in the American Apollo space programme. Apollo 13 should have been the third spacecraft to land on the Moon, but the 1970s trip was aborted following an on-board explosion. This was when astronauts were said to have uttered the famous words:

"Houston, we have a problem".

The moon has been arising,
the stars in golden guising
adorn the heavens bright.
The woods stand still in shadows,
and from the meads and meadows
lift whitish mists into the night.

Extract from a German lullaby
by Matthias Claudius

Moon Melodies

The song 'Fly Me to the Moon' was written in 1954 by American Bart Howard. It's been sung by many famous people including Nat King Cole, Ella Fitzgerald and Tony Bennett. But it was Frank Sinatra's 1964 recording that made the song really famous. His version was played on the Apollo 10 mission and became the first music to be played on the Moon, after astronaut Buzz Aldrin played it on a portable cassette player.

'Space Oddity' is a song written and recorded by British rock musician David Bowie, whose alter ego (a kind of alternative personality) was an alien from outer space called Ziggy Stardust! First released on 11th July 1969, just days before the first Moon landing, the song was inspired by the 1968 film *2001: A Space Odyssey*, by American director, screenwriter and producer Stanley Kubrick.

David Bowie's song tells the story of Major Tom, a fictional astronaut who cuts off communication with Earth, or 'Ground Control', and floats into space where he gets stranded. The British Broadcasting Corporation (BBC) used the song in its television coverage of the Moon landing – but there was a fear that if the missions didn't go well, the song might not be suitable.

The BBC mainly used the opening section of the classical music piece 'Also Sprach Zarathustra', during its coverage of the Moon landing. Created in 1896 by German composer Richard Strauss, it became associated with outer space after being used in the film *2001: A Space Odyssey*.

Perfect Paintings

Our shining Moon has been recorded by artists for many centuries in almost every country in the world, and not just in words.

Many symbolic images of the Moon survive in medieval and Renaissance works of art. Moon artwork from this time is usually shown as a crescent, and not many artists added any detail, apart from the Italian Leonardo da Vinci, who did a few rough sketches around 1500, and English physician William Gilbert, who sketched a detailed drawing of the Moon with his naked eye in the 1590s.

The Italian astronomer Galileo Galilei was also a master of drawing, using light and shadow. His art training may have helped him to understand earthshine (when sunlight reflected from Earth illuminates the darker portion of a crescent Moon).

His idea that the 'perfect' Moon could have mountains and valleys was new for his time and not accepted by everyone…

The Moon was usually a symbol of purity. The Virgin Mary was often shown in paintings on top of a perfectly smooth Moon, such as in *Immaculate Conception*, painted around 1660 by Italian painter Bartolomé Esteban Murillo.

However, Italian painter Lodovico Cardi, also known as Cigoli, was inspired by Galileo's findings. His last work, which he painted on the inside dome of the Pauline Chapel in Rome, showed Mary standing over a cratered Moon.

Chinese and Japanese Art

In traditional Chinese art, the Moon is usually shown as a tiny, distant object. The position of the Moon is said to give a sense of distance between the person looking at the painting and the Moon, allowing them to appreciate the calmness and stillness of it.

Japanese paintings, however, often show a large Moon, which is partly hidden by willow branches or clouds. During the Heian era (794–1185AD), Moon paintings became extremely widespread across Japan. Moon-viewing parties were also popular at this time.

Architecture

From the two-dimensional to the three-dimensional, the Moon has also inspired the design of many quirky-looking buildings…

The Crescent Development Project, or The Crescent Bay, is a huge skyscraper complex that is currently being built on the Caspian Sea coast in Baku, the capital city of Azerbaijan. The complex is made up of the Crescent Hotel (built on an artificial island), an office tower (Crescent City), a residential tower, and a retail and entertainment centre (Crescent Place). The 33-floor seven-star hotel has been designed to look like a crescent Moon with its points on the surface of the Caspian Sea. The crescent shape of the building reflects one of the main icons of Azerbaijan, as a crescent Moon appears on its national flag.

An unusual construction called Two Moon can be found outside Seoul, in South Korea. Designed by architect Moon Hoon, the venue is made up of two three-storey buildings, containing a coffee shop, gallery and spaces to rent.

The corner of each building has a crescent-like hole cut into it, which from certain angles appears to wax and wane from a crescent to a gibbous Moon; at other angles the two crescents appear to combine into a full Moon. Throughout the building, windows appear as full Moon shapes cut into the walls and ceilings.

CHAPTER SEVEN

One Giant Leap for Mankind

Konstantin Tsiolkovsky's rocket designs

Liquid hydrogen

Crew

Liquid oxygen

Carbon-dioxide
and vapour absorbers

1903

1914

Liquid oxygen
freely evaporating
at a very low temperature

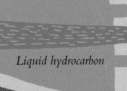

Crew,
breathing and other
equipment

Liquid hydrocarbon

1915

Rocket Revolution

There have been many fables and fantasies about travelling to the Moon, but finally fantasy became reality…

In the 1890s, Russian inventor Konstantin Tsiolkovsky was the first person to come up with the idea of launching a rocket to the Moon, and in 1903 he created the earliest known design of a liquid-fuelled rocket.

Konstantin Tsiolkovsky's initial rocket design, divided into three main sections, was the basis for modern spacecraft design. The pilot and co-pilot sat in the first section, while the second and third sections held the liquid oxygen and liquid hydrogen needed to fuel the spacecraft.

Sadly, Konstantin Tsiolkovsky never got to build his own rocket, but an American engineer called Robert H. Goddard did. In 1926, he launched the first ever liquid-fuelled rocket, although it only remained in flight for 2.5 seconds before landing in a cabbage field!

Between 1926 and 1941, Goddard and his team launched 34 rockets, reaching heights of 2.6km (1.6mi) and speeds of 885kmph (550mph). He also dreamed of seeing a rocket go to the Moon but sadly died before that happened. Although he wasn't around to see it, he certainly paved the way for space travel…

World War II, which lasted from 1939 to 1945, inspired further rocket development, which would eventually lead to space exploration and ultimately to the landing of humans on the Moon.

Germany was the first country to use a rocket-propelled weapon during the war when it launched its V-2 rocket in 1942 – invented by Wernher von Braun. After the war ended, Wernher von Braun surrendered to the US Army and his rocket technology was adapted and used for the US space programme. Meanwhile, rocket engineer and spacecraft designer Sergei Korolev led the way in Russia…

The   Space

In the late 1950s, the United States and the Soviet Union became very competitive and a space race began… Each wanted to be the first to put a man on the Moon. This was all going on during the time of the Cold War when political relations between the United States and the Soviet Union were already difficult.

At first, Russia appeared to be winning the space race when it launched Sputnik 1 on 4th October 1957. This aluminium sphere with a radio transmitter was the first man-made satellite to orbit Earth! It made America extremely anxious: if Russia could launch objects into Earth's orbit, then that meant it might also be capable of firing a bomb across the ocean!

When the United States tried to launch its first satellite into Earth's orbit on 6th December 1957, its Vanguard TV3 rocket exploded on the launch pad. Luckily, Wernher von Braun saved the day when his modified Jupiter-C rocket, Juno I, successfully launched America's Explorer 1 satellite into orbit on 31st January 1958.

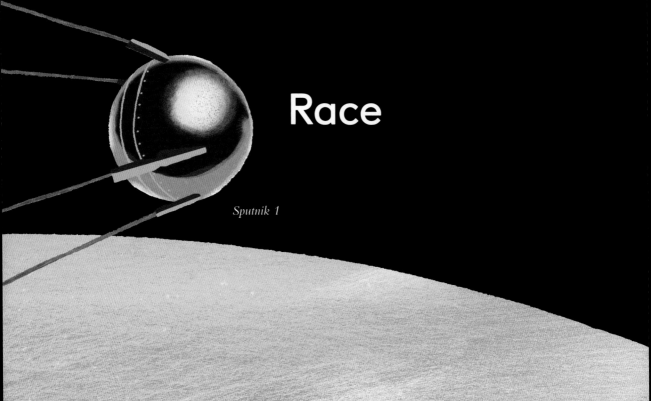

Race

Sputnik 1

Not long after Russia had launched Sputnik 1, the US government created an agency for space exploration in 1958. This agency was called the National Aeronautics and Space Administration (NASA).

Meanwhile, both countries were training their astronauts and developing their space technology. Then, on 25th May 1961, American President John F. Kennedy made a statement: by 1970, the United States would put astronauts into space and on the Moon. Sadly, Kennedy never lived to see his dream become reality, as he was assassinated in November 1963.

"First, I believe that this nation should commit itself to achieving the goal, before this decade is out, of landing a man on the Moon and returning him safely to the Earth. No single space project in this period will be more impressive to mankind, or more important for the long-range exploration of space; and none will be so difficult or expensive to accomplish."

President John F. Kennedy (statement to US Congress, 25th May 1961)

Unmanned Spacecraft

Before putting humans on the Moon, the United States and the Soviet Union had to carry out all kinds of unmanned missions. Firstly, they had to make sure that the technology would work. They also needed to map out the Moon and make sure that it would be possible to land on its surface.

The first unmanned spacecraft sent to the Moon were 'hard landers', or impact probes. They were designed to crash into the surface, whereas 'soft landers' were designed to touch down gently and to carry out further research on the Moon.

The Soviet Luna programme ran from 1959 until 1976. Out of the 24 spacecraft officially launched, 15 were successful. In January 1959, the Soviet Union launched Luna 1. It was supposed to be an impact probe but it missed the Moon by about 5,900km (3,666mi). Then, in September 1959 Luna 2 successfully crash-landed on the Moon's surface, becoming the first spacecraft ever to reach the Moon, and the first man-made object to land on another celestial body.

Then, in October 1959, Luna 3 took a trip around the back of the Moon and returned the first-ever photographs of its far side. This flyby probe took a total of 29 photographs from a distance of about 65,000km (40,000mi).

The probe only returned 17 of the shots, and although fuzzy, they caused great excitement! The pictures showed a surface that had many mountains, which was very different from the near side. It's believed that Luna 3 burned up in Earth's atmosphere in March or April 1960.

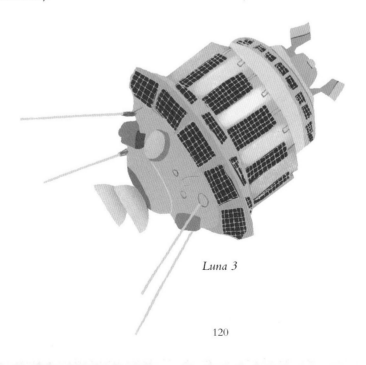

Luna 3

The Ranger programme was a series of unmanned space missions made by the United States in the 1960s. America wanted to get the first close-up images of the Moon's surface. The first six flights all failed. But in July 1964, Ranger 7 successfully returned 4,300 images during the final seventeen minutes of its flight before crashing on the Moon. Rangers 8 and 9 followed in 1965 – sending back even more images – of which some were broadcast live on television to millions of viewers across the United States.

Luna 9

The first spacecraft to make a soft landing on the Moon was the Soviet Union's Luna 9 in February 1966. It sent back nine images, including five black and white panorama (wide-view) photographs, which were the first shots taken from the Moon's surface.

In March–April 1966, the Soviet Union launched Luna 10, which became the first spacecraft to go into orbit around the Moon, and the first man-made object to orbit any celestial body beyond Earth. A compartment, which separated from the rest of the spacecraft, took three hours to complete each round trip of the Moon. The spacecraft transmitted back signals for 460 lunar orbits until the on-board batteries ran out. It gathered important data about radiation levels and rock formation.

Between 1966–7, the United States also sent five unmanned spacecraft to orbit the Moon during their Lunar Orbiter programme. They were looking for possible landing sites for their manned missions. All five missions were successful, and 99 per cent of the Moon was mapped from photographs taken by the spacecraft.

The United States also sent seven soft landers to the surface of the Moon. The Surveyor programme ran from 1966–8 and its purpose was to prove that the landers would not sink into the dust. Five of the landers successfully soft-landed on the Moon, while two failed. Surveyor 2 crashed at high speed into the Moon's surface, and it's believed that Surveyor 4 exploded just minutes before touchdown. All seven spacecraft are still on the Moon.

Getting There...

A very powerful and reliable rocket was needed to land people on the surface of the Moon, before returning them safely to Earth. And in October 1965 the Soviet space agency, OKB-1, planned to build one...

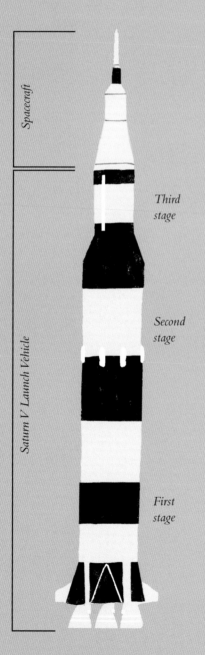

Spacecraft

Third stage

Second stage

First stage

Saturn V Launch Vehicle

The N1-L3 rocket was developed to compete with the United States' Apollo-Saturn V rocket and was expected to deliver a manned spacecraft onto the Moon's surface. The Soviet Union planned to launch the L3 spacecraft on a five-stage rocket (the N1). But this complicated project was doomed when its chief designer Sergei Korolev died in 1966. It was underfunded and rushed. Each of the four attempts to launch an N1 failed: in fact the second attempt destroyed the launch pad in one of the largest man-made non-nuclear explosions in history.

The N1 programme was suspended in 1974, and in 1976 was officially cancelled. The Soviet Moon mission had come to an end. The project was so secret that information about it wasn't published until 1989! The Soviet Union now concentrated on sending robotic spacecraft to the Moon instead of humans.

The United States came up with Saturn V. This was a three-stage liquid-fuelled rocket that NASA used from 1967–73 to support the Apollo programme, in which astronauts were sent to the Moon. Standing at about 110m (360ft) tall, the rocket was made up mainly of fuel and to this day remains the largest and most powerful rocket ever launched.

The first and second stages that made up the lower part of the rocket each had five engines and were designed to fall away when their fuel ran out. The third stage had just one engine and only separated once it had sent the Apollo spacecraft out of Earth orbit and on a course to the Moon.

Before the actual Moon landings could take place, NASA used Saturn V rockets to launch a number of Apollo spacecraft from Launch Complex 39 at the John F. Kennedy Space Center in Florida, USA. It took many years for NASA to finely tune the engines of its rocket design. Early versions of the Apollo spacecraft were launched on smaller Saturn rockets first (with just the third stage of the rocket).

The first complete Saturn V, with the unmanned Apollo 4 spacecraft, was sent into Earth orbit in November 1967 and was a success! All three stages separated as they should and their engines worked well. The third stage also restarted in orbit, which was essential for the lunar missions. At the end of the flight, the unmanned spacecraft re-entered Earth's atmosphere, proving it could survive the extreme heat generated during a high-speed return from the Moon. All was set for future Apollo missions and eventually landing humans on the Moon…

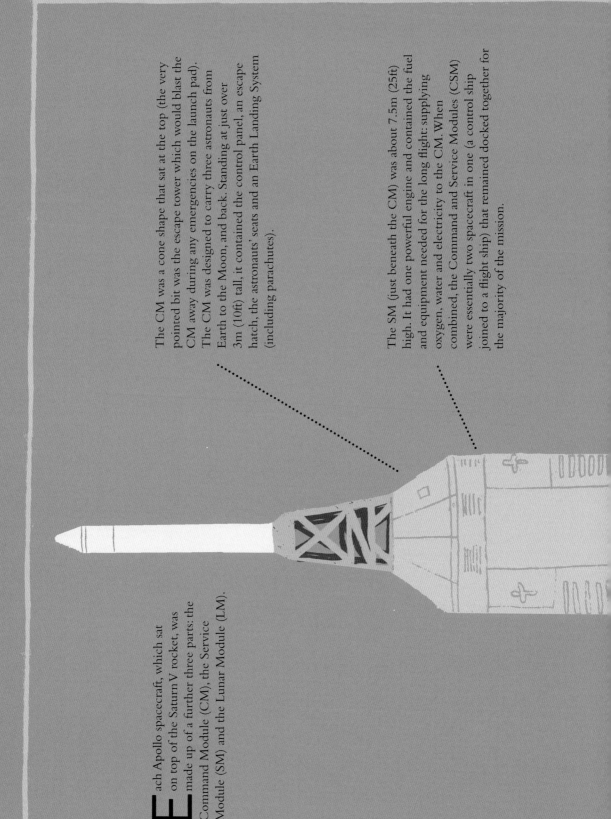

Each Apollo spacecraft, which sat on top of the Saturn V rocket, was made up of a further three parts: the Command Module (CM), the Service Module (SM) and the Lunar Module (LM).

The CM was a cone shape that sat at the top (the very pointed bit was the escape tower which would blast the CM away during any emergencies on the launch pad). The CM was designed to carry three astronauts from Earth to the Moon, and back. Standing at just over 3m (10ft) tall, it contained the control panel, an escape hatch, the astronauts' seats and an Earth Landing System (including parachutes).

The SM (just beneath the CM) was about 7.5m (25ft) high. It had one powerful engine and contained the fuel and equipment needed for the long flight: supplying oxygen, water and electricity to the CM. When combined, the Command and Service Modules (CSM) were essentially two spacecraft in one (a control ship joined to a flight ship) that remained docked together for the majority of the mission.

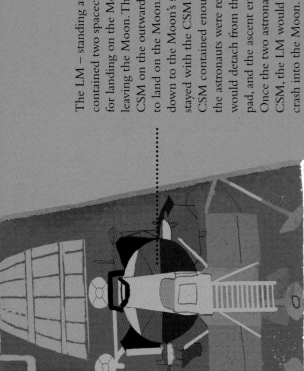

The LM – standing at about 7m (23ft) tall – also contained two spacecraft in one: the descent stage used for landing on the Moon; topped with an ascent stage for leaving the Moon. The whole LM was attached to the CSM on the outward journey, and would then separate to land on the Moon. While two of the astronauts went down to the Moon's surface in the LM, one of them stayed with the CSM in orbit around the Moon (the CSM contained enough fuel to return to Earth). When the astronauts were ready to leave the Moon, the LM would detach from the descent stage, using it as a launch pad, and the ascent engine would fire back into orbit. Once the two astronauts had cocked once again with the CSM, the LM would detach and fly into outer space or crash into the Moon.

On the return journey to Earth, the CM containing the astronauts (and protected by a heat shield) would separate from the SM and enter Earth's atmosphere. The CM would then land safely in the sea, using its parachutes.

The astronauts often named the different parts of their Apollo spacecraft. Those aboard Apollo 11 (the first spacecraft to fly to the Moon) named the CSM Columbia after the Columbiad – the giant cannon in Jules Verne's novel *From the Earth to the Moon*. The LM was named Eagle after the United States' national bird, the bald eagle.

Amazing Astronauts

M. Scott Carpenter

While the technology that put humans on the Moon was extremely impressive, it was the bravery of the astronauts that played a huge part in the success of space travel...

The Mercury Seven, or the Original Seven, or Astronaut Group 1, were the first American astronauts chosen to lead the US human spaceflight programme in 1959.

They were: M. Scott Carpenter, L. Gordon Cooper, John Glenn, Virgil I. 'Gus' Grissom, Walter Schirra, Alan Shepard and Donald 'Deke' Slayton.

L. Gordon Cooper

The programme aimed to put an astronaut into Earth orbit in a one-person spacecraft (John Glenn was the first American to achieve this) and was an experiment to test whether humans could survive space travel – the seven members made history, and the public adored them.

The astronauts piloted the manned spaceflights of the Mercury programme from May 1961 to May 1963, although many were involved in other NASA manned missions of the 20th century, including Project Gemini, Project Apollo and the Space Shuttle.

John Glenn

Virgil I. 'Gus' Grissom

Walter Schirra

Alan Shepard

Donald 'Deke' Slayton

Project Gemini was NASA's second human spaceflight programme that began in 1961, and was the next step that led to the Apollo Moon landings. The Gemini spacecraft carried a crew of two. The aim of the programme was to develop space-travel techniques and to prepare astronauts to land on the Moon, including how to dock spacecraft and carry out spacewalks. Between March 1965 and November 1966, there were ten manned Gemini flights.

Missions Unaccomplished

Sadly, not every mission ended well… Apollo 1 was the first manned mission of the US Apollo programme, which aimed to land on the Moon. NASA planned to launch Apollo 1 on 21st February 1967, but then tragedy struck. A cabin fire during a launch test on 27th January killed all three astronauts on board, including Virgil I. 'Gus' Grissom. The fire was caused by the electrics and spread quickly. Manned Apollo flights were suspended for 18 months while the hazards were addressed.

Apollo 13 was the seventh manned Apollo mission and should have been the third spacecraft to land on the Moon. It launched on 11th April 1970 but the lunar landing was aborted after an oxygen tank exploded two days later. The SM, upon which the CM depended, was useless, with limited power and oxygen, loss of cabin heat and a shortage of water. Despite this, the crew managed to return safely to Earth six days later. Apollo 13 even flew around the far side of the Moon, achieving a world record for the furthest distance from Earth reached by humans: 254km (158mi) above the Moon's surface, and 400,171km (248,655mi) from our planet.

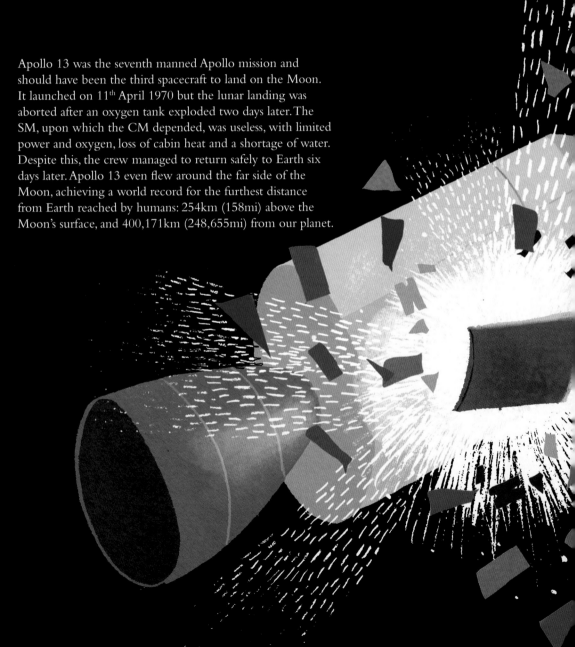

The Russians had problems too...

The Soviet's Soyuz 11 was the only manned mission to board the world's first space station, Salyut 1. A space station is a large artificial satellite that orbits Earth, in which astronauts live for long periods of time in order to carry out research and experiments.

When Soyuz 11 arrived at the space station on 7th June 1971, it was a small victory for Russia after America had successfully landed men on the Moon. However, during their return journey on 30th June, the three cosmonauts suffered rapid decompression (when gas gets into the blood). This may have been caused when one of two valves at the top of the descent module opened too early; or a leak came from the hatch. The crew were the only humans to have died in space.

More Space Firsts

Some amazing feats took place during the American and Russian space programmes, but there was nothing quite like being the first one to reap the glory!

On 12th April 1961, Soviet cosmonaut Yuri Gagarin achieved one of the greatest moments in space-travel history when he became the first human in outer space aboard spacecraft Vostok 1. Vostok 1 travelled once around Earth, reaching a maximum height of 327km (203mi).

Before Yuri Gagarin's historic flight, the Soviet Union launched a couple of test spacecraft, together with a life-size dummy called Ivan Ivanovich and real-life dogs. Despite these early tests, the engineers had not yet developed a braking system that would slow the craft enough for a human to survive the landing impact. And so Yuri Gagarin had to eject himself before parachuting down to Earth.

Alan Shepard became the first American man in space, when on 5th May 1961 he made the first Project Mercury flight in a spacecraft he named Freedom 7. His spacecraft did not go into orbit, but Alan Shepard did become the first person to manually control the direction of his spacecraft.

It was John Glenn (another member of the original Mercury Seven) who was the first American to orbit Earth, circling it three times, in February 1962.

The first woman in space

On 16th June 1963, Russian cosmonaut Valentina Tereshkova became the first woman in space when she flew in Vostok 6. She was selected from more than 400 applicants! Valentina Tereshkova completed 48 orbits of Earth and spent almost three days in space. Before becoming a cosmonaut, she worked in a textile factory and was an amateur skydiver. In 2013, she volunteered to go on a one-way trip to Mars if the opportunity ever arises…

On 18th March 1965, Soviet cosmonaut Alexey Leonov became the first human to exit his spacecraft and walk in outer space. For twelve minutes and nine seconds, he floated free of the Voskhod 2 spacecraft on a long white cord. It was a risky mission, in which he almost suffered heatstroke.

On 21st December 1968 the American Apollo 8 mission took astronauts around the Moon for the first time – they got to see the far side! The astronauts, who sent back photographs of Earth from outer space, were also the first people to see Earth 'rise' over the Moon.

Animals in Space

In the early days of space travel, it was important for scientists to investigate the biological effects that such an environment might have on the human body. To achieve this, many animals were used to test the idea of sending human beings into space and bringing them back safely.

Some of the biological functions studied on the animals included looking at how their brains and hearts reacted, as well as the behaviour of the animals themselves when they experienced exposure to radiation or weightlessness (which happens to the astronauts because they are travelling through space at the same speed as their surroundings).

On 14th June 1949 Albert II became the first monkey in space. He was sent up on a V-2 rocket launched by the United States. He reached a height of about 134km (83mi) but sadly died on his return trip to Earth after a parachute failed to work.
He was the United States' second attempt to send a monkey into space. The first monkey, called Albert I, reached a maximum height of 63km (39mi) on 11th June 1948 before dying of suffocation during the flight.

The first living creature to orbit Earth was a dog called Laika. On 3rd November 1957, the Russian cosmonaut dog was sent on a one-way trip aboard the Soviet Union's Sputnik 2. Technology to return the spacecraft to Earth and 'de-orbit' had not yet been developed and about five to seven hours into the flight, it was feared that Laika was no longer alive.

The truth about Laika's death was not made public until 2002. Previous reports had said that she died when her oxygen ran out or that she was put to sleep. Laika's spacecraft circled Earth 2,570 times before burning up in Earth's atmosphere in April 1958. Laika only survived for a few hours, but the mission helped to prove that a living passenger could survive being launched into orbit with low levels of gravity, and paved the way for human spaceflight.

On 31st January 1961, Ham the chimpanzee became
the first animal to interact with a spacecraft when he
was launched in one of the Project Mercury capsules.
Ham was named after the Holloman Aerospace
Medical Center in New Mexico, USA, the lab that
prepared him for his mission. He was trained to pull
levers in return for banana pellets. The spacecraft
suffered some loss of pressure during the mission, but
Ham's spacesuit protected him. After a 16-minute flight,
the spacecraft splashed down in the Atlantic Ocean and
Ham was picked up by a rescue ship. He went on to
live for another 17 years.

French scientists launched the first cat into space on
18th October 1963. The black and white Parisian cat,
named Félicette, was sent on a Véronique AGI 47
rocket. The non-orbital flight lasted for 15 minutes
and reached a height of 156km (97mi). Félicette was
successfully saved when the capsule parachuted back
down to Earth.

On 9th November 1970, NASA sent two bullfrogs
into orbit in order to study weightlessness and how
it affected balance. These particular frogs had a mini
spacecraft designed specifically for them, measuring just
76cm (30in) x 119cm (47in). Bullfrogs were chosen
as their ear bones are very similar to those of humans.
Unfortunately for the frogs, the project was a one-way
mission. But the experiment was successful, showing
the frogs to be in good health throughout the flight.

Even spiders have made it into space! On 28th July
1973, two garden spiders named Arabella and Anita
went into orbit as part of NASA's Skylab 3 mission.
Since the spider uses its own weight to decide the
thickness of web it needs, gravity plays a vital part in its
web-building. It took a few days, but the spiders were
soon spinning webs as if back on Earth. Although finer,
the patterns of the webs were the same.

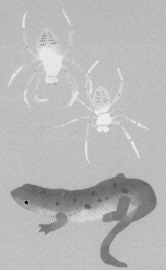

Bion 7, also known as Kosmos 1667, was a biomedical
research mission satellite. On 10th July 1985, ten newts
flew aboard Bion 7 for seven days. Parts of their limbs
were amputated to see if they would regrow, as they do
on Earth. It turned out that the newts' limbs regrew
much faster in space than they could on Earth.

The Biggest 'First' of All

About a month after the Apollo 8 mission made history in December 1968, when it carried astronauts around the far side of the Moon, Donald 'Deke' Slayton (one of the original Mercury Seven) met with astronauts Neil Armstrong, Edwin 'Buzz' Aldrin and Michael Collins. As Director of Flight Crew Operations, Donald 'Deke' Slayton played a big part in the Apollo programme and in picking the crews. If all went well with the Apollo 9 and 10 test flights, then it would be these astronauts who would fly to the Moon in Apollo 11.

In the lead-up to the mission, the astronauts spent many hours training. Then, on 16th July 1969, they were finally ready to climb aboard the Saturn V rocket at the John F. Kennedy Space Center. Once the rocket had launched Apollo 11, it took a few days for the crew to fly to the Moon – and so the astronauts waited patiently in their Command Module.

As the astronauts got closer to the Moon, Neil Armstrong described the view to NASA's Mission Control Center:

"The view of the Moon that we've been having recently is really spectacular... It's a view worth the price of the trip."

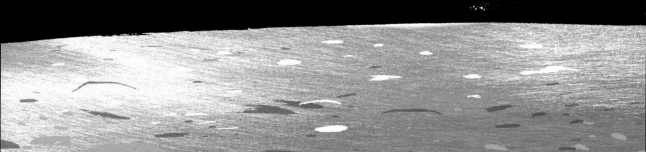

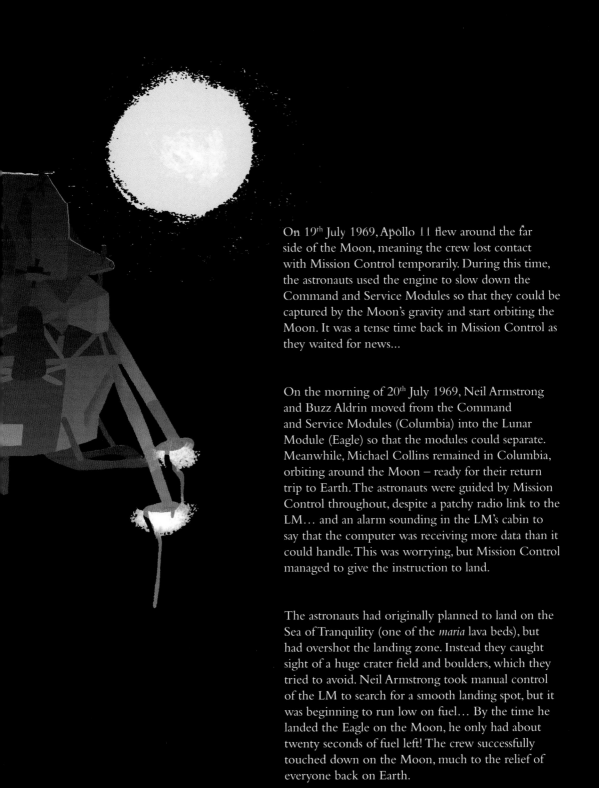

On 19th July 1969, Apollo 11 flew around the far
side of the Moon, meaning the crew lost contact
with Mission Control temporarily. During this time,
the astronauts used the engine to slow down the
Command and Service Modules so that they could be
captured by the Moon's gravity and start orbiting the
Moon. It was a tense time back in Mission Control as
they waited for news...

On the morning of 20th July 1969, Neil Armstrong
and Buzz Aldrin moved from the Command
and Service Modules (Columbia) into the Lunar
Module (Eagle) so that the modules could separate.
Meanwhile, Michael Collins remained in Columbia,
orbiting around the Moon – ready for their return
trip to Earth. The astronauts were guided by Mission
Control throughout, despite a patchy radio link to the
LM… and an alarm sounding in the LM's cabin to
say that the computer was receiving more data than it
could handle. This was worrying, but Mission Control
managed to give the instruction to land.

The astronauts had originally planned to land on the
Sea of Tranquility (one of the *maria* lava beds), but
had overshot the landing zone. Instead they caught
sight of a huge crater field and boulders, which they
tried to avoid. Neil Armstrong took manual control
of the LM to search for a smooth landing spot, but it
was beginning to run low on fuel… By the time he
landed the Eagle on the Moon, he only had about
twenty seconds of fuel left! The crew successfully
touched down on the Moon, much to the relief of
everyone back on Earth.

The Eagle Has Landed

In the early hours of 21ˢᵗ July 1969, Neil Armstrong opened the Eagle's hatch, watched by at least 600 million people around the world live on television. On his way down the ladder, he uncovered a plaque mounted on the LM descent stage. It read:

HERE MEN FROM THE PLANET EARTH
FIRST SET FOOT UPON THE MOON
JULY 1969, A.D.
WE CAME IN PEACE FOR ALL MANKIND

Neil Armstrong described the Moon's surface as fine and powdery. Six and a half hours after landing, he took his first steps on the Moon and famously said:

"That's one small step for man, one giant leap for mankind."

Walking on the Moon

Neil Armstrong found that he could walk around easily, albeit slowly, due to the Moon having one-sixth of Earth's gravity. He quickly picked up a soil sample in case an emergency meant that he had to return to the LM. Buzz Aldrin climbed down almost 20 minutes after Neil Armstrong. After planting a specially designed US flag on the Moon's surface, both astronauts spoke to President Richard M. Nixon who had called from Earth:

"For one priceless moment in the whole history of man, all the people on this Earth are truly one: one in their pride in what you have done, and one in our prayers that you will return safely to Earth."

The astronauts picked up 21.55kg (47.5lb) of Moon rock and soil to bring back to Earth. Three new minerals were discovered – one of which was named Armalcolite after Armstrong, Aldrin and Collins.

They set up experiments and took photographs. After walking on the Moon for more than two hours, the astronauts prepared to lift off after catching up on some sleep. After about seven hours of rest, Mission Control woke the crew to prepare for the return flight. Two and a half hours later, Neil Armstrong and Buzz Aldrin lifted off in Eagle's ascent stage to dock once again with Columbia, where Michael Collins was waiting to take them home.

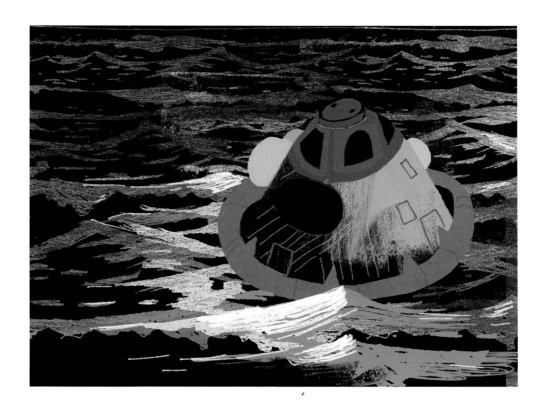

On 23rd July 1969 (the last night before splash-down), the astronauts spoke to the people back home who were watching on television and thanked everyone involved in the mission – of which there were around 400,000 people!

On 24th July 1969, just over a week after the astronauts began their trip, they returned home aboard Columbia. It was another tense moment as everyone watched their safe re-entry into Earth's atmosphere. Apollo 11 splashed down in the Pacific Ocean where the astronauts were then taken to the recovery ship, *USS Hornet*.

The men spent almost three weeks in quarantine to make sure they hadn't brought diseases back from the Moon. On 13th August 1969, they took part in parades in New York, Chicago and Los Angeles. They were now national heroes as America celebrated winning the space race!

What Happened Next?

The Americans had won the space race. So what happened next? Even though the Soviet Union had fallen behind after the death of rocket scientist Sergei Korolev, they were still keen to learn more about the Moon, sending robotic craft to explore it in place of humans…

A major achievement of the Soviet's Luna programme was Luna 16. In September 1970, it was the first robotic probe to land on the Moon and bring back a sample of lunar soil to Earth. The sample came from the Mare Fecunditatis, meaning 'Sea of Fertility', on the near side of the Moon. The sample was so valuable that, in 1993, three seed-sized pieces of it − 0.2g (0.007oz) − were sold at Sotheby's auction house in New York for $442,500!

Other unmanned robotic craft soon followed, and successfully returned Moon samples: Luna 20, in February 1972, and Luna 24, in August 1976. In total, the three missions managed to bring back just over 300g (0.66lb) of lunar-soil samples.

While the Russians were busy with robotic spacecraft, the American Apollo manned missions still continued… There were five more Apollo Moon landings after Apollo 11, ending with Apollo 17 in December 1972. Each of the missions explored different landscapes on the Moon's near side.

Apollo 15 was an important mission for many reasons. The United States called it a 'J mission', meaning the astronauts would spend longer on the Moon. They spent three days in total, allowing them to carry out more experiments than previously possible.

It was also the first Apollo mission to use the Lunar Roving Vehicle, or Moon buggy. This was a battery-powered four-wheeled vehicle that could carry two astronauts and their equipment over the Moon's surface. Lunar Roving Vehicles were used in all three of the last Apollo missions during 1971 and 1972, and the three Lunar Roving Vehicles are still on the Moon to this day.

Lunar Roving Vehicle, Apollo 15

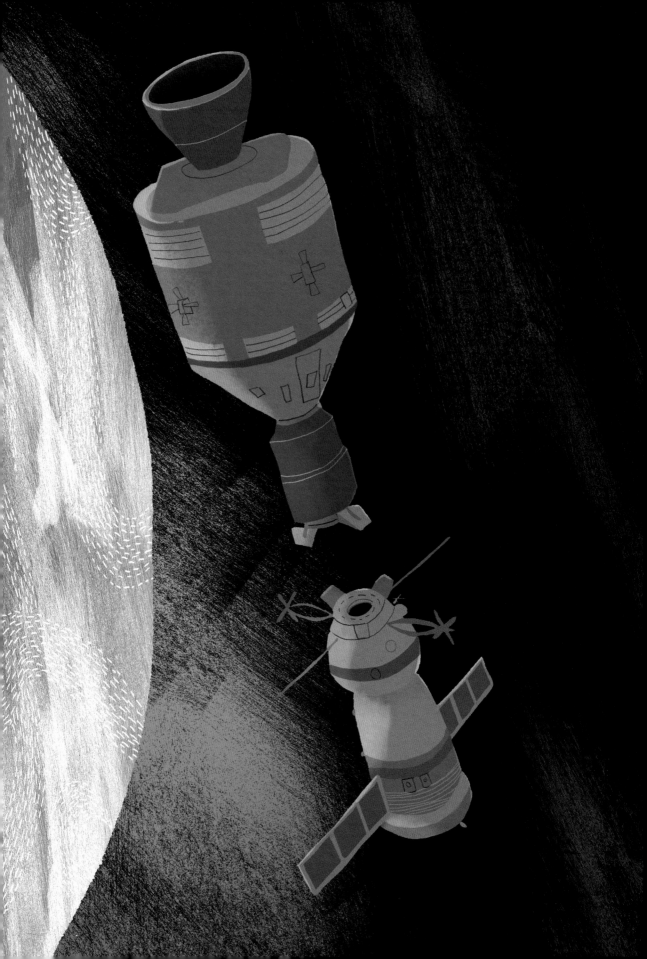

More Moon Missions

The Soviet Union launched a couple of their own lunar rovers to the Moon, using unmanned spacecraft, in what was known as the Lunokhod programme. The original Lunokhod, set for February 1969, was destroyed when its rocket disintegrated a couple of seconds after launch. However, Lunokhod 1 in 1970 and Lunokhod 2 in 1973 successfully reached the Moon. The remote-controlled Lunokhods were used to explore the lunar surface and to take photographs.

Then, in July 1975, the United States and Soviet Union worked together on the Apollo-Soyuz Test Project (ASTP). It was the first joint US-Soviet spaceflight and marked the end of poor political relations…

First, the Soviet's Soyuz spacecraft, Soyuz 19, launched into Earth orbit on 15th July with two cosmonauts on board. Then seven-and-a-half hours later, the United States launched their Apollo Command and Service Modules with three astronauts on board. On 17th July, the two craft docked together for two days. Both sides worked jointly and separately on various experiments and the mission provided valuable engineering experience for future joint US-Soviet spaceflights. It was also US astronaut Donald 'Deke' Slayton's only spaceflight (he had been grounded until 1972 for medical reasons).

The ASTP was the last manned US space mission until the first Space Shuttle flight that took place in April 1981. The Space Shuttle programme, or Space Transportation System (STS) ran from 1981 to 2011 – the United States' answer to cheaper space travel. The space shuttles never actually flew to the Moon but the same crafts could be used to go into Earth orbit again and again.

After the Soviet's Luna 24, many years passed before another spacecraft actually went to the Moon…

And then Japan began exploring it. The Hiten Spacecraft built by the Institute of Space and Astronautical Science of Japan was launched on 24th January 1990. It was Japan's first lunar probe, and the first lunar probe launched by a country other than the Soviet Union or the United States. The probe swung by the Moon and, after some initial problems, eventually orbited it before being deliberately crashed into the surface on 10th April 1993.

The first US mission to return to the Moon after Apollo was Clementine, launched on 25th January 1994. Clementine was a joint space project between the Ballistic Missile Defense Organization (BMDO) and NASA. The mission involved two months spent mapping the Moon, capturing more than 1.8 million digital images. When scientists reviewed Clementine's data, they discovered possible signs of ice in the Moon's polar craters, which was confirmed by NASA following their Lunar Prospector mission (January 1998–July 1999).

CHAPTER EIGHT

Back
Down
to
Earth

Mapping the Moon Through History

I n the early 17th century, telescopes allowed astronomers to begin making detailed maps of the Moon and all of its features – they could even begin naming parts of the surface.

Italian astronomer Galileo Galilei was one of the first people to point a telescope at the Moon in 1609 and to make detailed drawings of it. English astronomer Thomas Harriot had studied the Moon through a telescope several months earlier, but he never published his findings. After building his own telescope in 1609, Galileo Galilei went on to create improved versions with better magnification. And in 1610, he spotted the mountains and craters on the Moon. He published his sketches in a pamphlet called *Sidereus Nuncius* (*Starry Messenger*).

The first telescopes used by Thomas Harriot and Galileo Galilei had a narrow field of view, meaning that only a small portion of the Moon could be seen at any one time – making their work all the more impressive.

One of the first works to be considered a true map of the Moon was made in 1645 by Dutch astronomer Michael Florent van Langren. Using a telescope, he was the first one to give names to the light and dark areas of the Moon. He labelled the light areas: *terra* (meaning 'Earth' or 'land') and the dark areas *mare* (meaning 'sea'). He also named some of the craters after royalty, as well as famous astronomers and mathematicians.

In 1647, German astronomer Johannes Hevelius published a rival work called *Selenographia*, considered to be the first comprehensive atlas of the Moon. He even built his own observatory on the roofs of his three connected houses! His work influenced many European astronomers of the period, and his atlas was used as a 'go to' reference for over a century.

Johannes Hevelius gave many new names to the Moon's mountains, seas and craters, borrowing some from Earth, such as the Alps. Some of these names are still in use today but most have been replaced by Italian astronomer Giovanni Riccioli's naming system that he published in his book *Almagestum Novum* in 1651. One name originated by Riccioli was *Mare Tranquillitatis* (Sea of Tranquility).

Johannes Hevelius

Lunar Images

Later astronomers and lunar mappers added even more names for the Moon's mountains, seas and craters. German astronomer Johann Schröter published a highly detailed map of the Moon in his 1791 book: *Selenotopographische Fragmente zur genauern Kenntniss der Mondfläche* (*Topographical Fragments For a Better Knowledge of the Lunar Surface*). He discovered the largest sinuous rille, or valley, on the Moon in 1787. It's called Schröter's Valley, while the start of it is nicknamed 'Cobra's Head' as it looks a bit like a snake!

The first map

The first exact map of the Moon, *Mappa Selenographica*, was published in four volumes between 1834–6. It was created by wealthy German banker Wilhelm Beer and German astronomer Johann Mädler. Both came to the conclusion that the Moon had no atmosphere or water (although they were later proved wrong).

The first photograph

It wasn't just early telescopes that were impressive for the time. The very first photograph of the Moon was made in 1839 by French inventor Louis Daguerre – using his daguerreotype process (a unique image on a silver-coated copper plate). Unfortunately, a couple of months later, his entire laboratory burnt to the ground, destroying the historical image. Then in 1840, John William Draper, an English-American scientist, took his own daguerreotype of the Moon, said to be the very first detailed photograph of it.

Giant telescopes

In September 1959, the giant Lovell Telescope – a huge white bowl with a diameter of 76.2m (250ft) – helped track the Luna 2 mission and provided scientific proof that it had successfully crashed on the Moon. The telescope is part of the British Jodrell Bank Observatory in Manchester, which helped track space probes at the start of the Space Age.

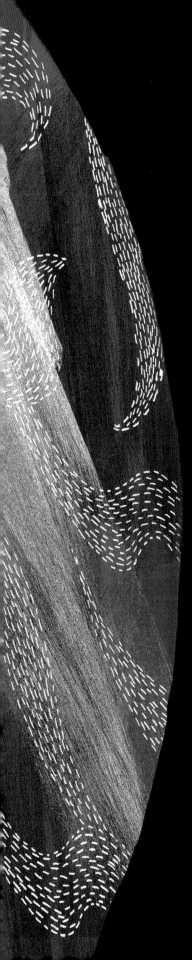

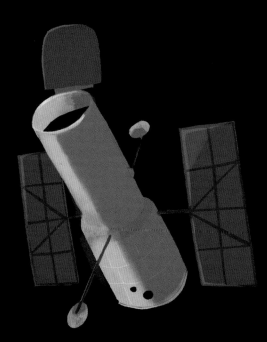

Telescopes are not just on Earth! Some are up in space and orbit Earth, such as NASA's Hubble Space Telescope, which was launched into low Earth orbit in 1990. It has taken some of the most detailed photographs that we have of space.

In the past, NASA has used the Hubble Space Telescope to hunt for oxygen sources on the Moon. As oxygen is essential for life, they wanted to know if humans could eventually live on the Moon. The telescope uses ultraviolet light to find oxygen that can be extracted from the soils. As it happens, there is oxygen in the Moon's rocks and soil, which could be used for breathing and for rocket fuel. Since ultraviolet light is blocked by gases in Earth's atmosphere, ground-based telescopes can't be used to look at the Moon's surface in this way.

CHAPTER **NINE**

The
Moon
Today

Elderly Moon

It is 4.5 billion years old, so just how is our elderly Moon faring up there in the sky?

Believe it or not, astronomers have spotted wrinkles all over the Moon's surface. These wrinkles, called 'lobate scarps', are cliffs that have formed on the Moon's crust. The cliffs were discovered when a team examined the detailed photographs taken by NASA's Lunar Reconnaissance Orbiter (LRO), which captures images as it orbits the Moon.

Astronomers think that the cliffs were caused because the Moon is shrinking (in fact, they believe it has lost 200m (656ft) from its diameter). When the Moon first formed it had an extremely hot core, much like Earth's, which caused it to expand and then to shrink as it cooled down. But the latest findings suggest that the Moon could still be cooling and is therefore shrinking…

Fourteen new cliffs were captured by the LRO. The features were so clear, and unmarked by craters, that scientists think they could be no more than a billion years old – or even as young as a hundred million years. This might sound very old, but it is less than 25 per cent of the Moon's current age, and so is fairly recent in Moon terms!

The largest cliff is about 90m (300ft) high and is several kilometres long, but the majority are short in length and height. Many of the cliffs are semi-circular or lobe-shaped, which is why they are called 'lobate scarps'.

The seismometers left on the Moon by the Apollo missions have recorded moonquakes. It's thought that most of these quakes were caused by changing day-and-night temperatures, the gravitational pull of Earth, or impacts by meteoroids and asteroids, but scientists also think that some moonquakes might be caused by scarp formation – the Moon's wrinkles!

On the Move

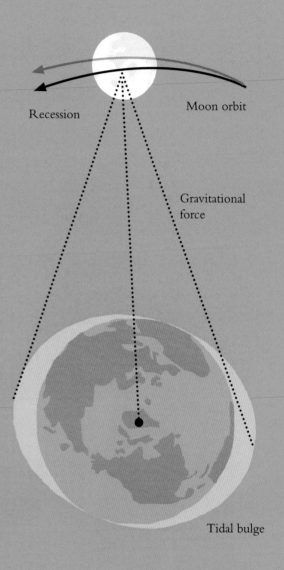

id you know that the Moon is moving further away from us? Every year, it creeps away by about 3.78cm (1.5in) – about the same speed at which your fingernails grow.

It's believed that when the Moon first formed, it was much closer to Earth – about 22,500km (13,980mi) away. If you compare that with the average distance that the Moon is now from Earth – about 384,400km (238,855mi) – you'll see how much it has moved…

Recession

Moon orbit

Gravitational force

Why is the Moon moving away?

It's mainly down to Earth's tides. We know that the Moon is kept in orbit due to Earth's gravitational pull; and that the Moon has a gravitational pull on Earth that causes tides or tidal bulges.

Because Earth rotates faster on its axis (once every 24 hours) than the Moon orbits Earth (once every 27.32 days), the tidal bulge tries to 'speed up' the Moon by pulling it ahead. This puts the Moon into a higher orbit, making it move further away from Earth. This process is known as recession.

It's like being on a roundabout. The faster the roundabout spins, the more you feel as if you're being thrown outwards. At the same time, the Moon pulls back on the tidal bulge of Earth, slowing Earth's rotation.

Tidal bulge

How does this affect life on our planet?

When the Moon had just formed, days on Earth were about five hours long. However, because the Moon has caused Earth to spin more slowly over the last 4.5 billion years, our days have become much longer. Imagine what might happen to a spinning plate if it slowed down too much – it would start to wobble! If planet Earth wobbles this could affect its tilt, which in turn could affect our seasons, leading to freezing winters and blazing hot summers.

We could probably adapt as humans, but the wildlife might not be so lucky. Who knows – in a few billion years, the human race may be living on another planet anyway…

The Moon itself has tilted slightly over time, meaning that the Man in the Moon (when viewed from ancient Earth) may have looked a little different to how he does now. In fact, he's said to have turned his nose up at Earth!

Scientists think that this small shift in position was caused billions of years ago by volcanic activity in the Moon's mantle (the deep layer of rock beneath the crust). As the mantle heated up, it expanded and decreased in density (or solidity) as lava erupted from the surface – imagine removing a chunk from one side of a football and seeing how it would change its spin through the air. The change in tilt also caused the Moon's north and south poles to shift over time – due to the Sun's light landing at a different angle, therefore melting the more ancient poles.

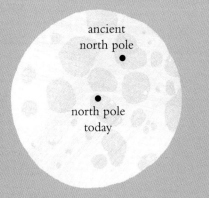

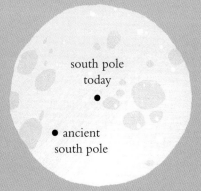

Who's Exploring Now?

The human race appears to remain fascinated by the Moon. While humans have not stepped on it since the Apollo missions, many countries are still continuing with programmes to explore it – with hopes of eventually sending people there again one day, maybe to stay...

The European Space Agency (ESA) is an organisation dedicated to space exploration. It is made up of 22 member states, including France, Germany, Italy and the United Kingdom. On 27th September 2003 the agency launched SMART-1 into orbit around the Moon – its first Moon mission, which lasted until 3rd September 2006. The goal was to test new technologies and to examine the Moon's origin, its volcanic activity and the possible existence of ice.

The Aurora programme is a human spaceflight programme set up by the ESA in 2001. One of its goals has been to develop human spaceflight in order to investigate moons and planets with the possibility of living on them in the future. The ESA has suggested humans may travel to Mars by 2025, using the Moon as a stop-off point.

On 14th September 2007, the Japan Aerospace Exploration Agency (JAXA) launched its unmanned lunar orbit explorer, Kaguya (named after a Moon princess in Japanese folklore).

The mission, also known as SELENE, was the largest Moon mission since the Apollo programme. After gathering data on the Moon's origin and how the Moon has changed over time, it crashed into the lunar surface on 10th June 2009. The mission included two baby satellites (named Okina and Ouna, also after characters in the tale). Their job was to map the gravitational field (or gravitational pull) of the Moon.

In 2019, JAXA plans to land its first unmanned craft on the Moon. SLIM (Smart Lander for Investigating Moon) is designed to pinpoint exactly where to land, recognising lunar craters by using the same technology as facial recognition systems. Japan hopes to use its probes to study the possible use of materials on the Moon as well as its environment, which might lead to future manned missions in 2025.

CLEP

The Chinese Lunar Exploration
Programme (CLEP), also known as the
Chang'e programme after the Chinese
Moon goddess, is the name for a number
of robotic Moon missions by the China
National Space Administration (CNSA).
The programme includes lunar orbiters,
landers and rovers, and spacecraft that
return with Moon samples. It began on 24th
October 2007 when China launched its
first unmanned Moon orbiter, Chang'e 1.

Chang'e 1 has produced the most detailed
3D map of the lunar surface ever created.
The orbiter was crashed into the Moon's
surface on 1st March 2009. The unmanned
mission Chang'e 3 included a robotic lander
and China's first lunar rover. It landed on
the Moon on 14th December 2013 – the
first spacecraft to soft-land on the Moon
since the Soviet Union's Luna 24 in 1976.

The CLEP logo looks like a lunar crescent
curved around two human footprints – it
represents the main goal of the programme:
to put humans on the Moon, possibly
during 2025–30.

中国探月

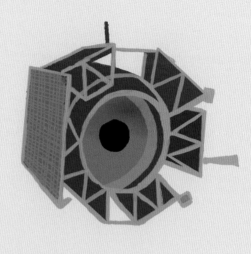

ISRO

On 22nd October 2008, the Indian Space Research Organisation (ISRO) launched its first mission: Chandrayaan-1, which included an unmanned lunar orbiter and an impact probe. Chandrayaan-1 became the first lunar mission to officially discover water on the Moon's surface.

Chandrayaan-1 carried some of NASA's instruments with it, which detected the water, mainly found at the Moon's north and south poles. It also discovered widespread water on the Moon when water molecules were detected in the lunar soil. The findings were very important as they show that humans could one day survive for long periods on the Moon and manned bases could possibly be built there.

LCROSS

In June 2009, NASA sent a robotic spacecraft (the Lunar Crater Observation and Sensing Satellite (LCROSS) to follow up on Chandrayaan-1's discovery of water on the Moon. It was launched with the Lunar Reconnaissance Orbiter (LRO) and successfully confirmed that there was water in the southern lunar crater 'Cabeus'. The results from this mission may possibly lead to the United States setting up groups of people (colonies) on the Moon one day…

It seems Russia hasn't given up on sending people to the Moon just yet… Apparently it is planning to build a rocket called Ryov that will transport astronauts from the International Space Station (ISS) to the Moon – and maybe even Mars. They hope to do this by the year 2029.

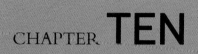

CHAPTER **TEN**

The Moon and the Future

Living on the Moon...

With advances in technology, along with increased concerns over humanity's future on Earth (because of its changing climate and shortage of resources), the idea of setting up human colonies on the Moon seems to make sense.

And it's one that NASA thinks might be possible by the year 2022, or at least an initial Moon base to start with – housing up to ten people – before establishing a settlement of 100 people within the following ten years.

Cost has been a major reason why humans haven't stepped on the Moon since 1969 (the Apollo programme would cost about $150 billion (£120 billion) in today's money. But NASA thinks it would be possible to send a small group of astronauts to the Moon for just $10 billion (£8 billion) and to set up a more permanent Moon base for just $40 billion (£32 billion).

But how would this be possible?

Many of the technologies needed already exist on the International Space Station (ISS) and back on Earth.

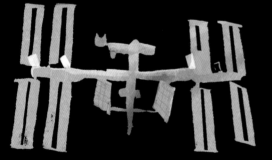

The International Space Station orbits Earth and is the world's largest group venture in science and technology between European countries (represented by ESA), the United States (NASA), Japan (JAXA), Canada (CSA) and Russia (Roscosmos).

Self-driving cars and green-toilet technology (recycling waste into fertiliser), which have been developed on Earth, could be adapted for life on the Moon. Survey robots could pinpoint the perfect spot for a Moon base by analysing the surface and the resources available; and water and air-recycling systems that keep astronauts alive on the International Space Station could be used.

The first base on the Moon might be constructed using robots and 3D printing. The robots would lay down many thin layers of lunar soil to build the base, by following a three-dimensional digital model. Another option for shelter would be inflatable habitats or tents.

It's thought that plants could even be grown within the Moon base in sand or gravel, using the waste from tilapia fish (fish that live in slightly salty water) to feed the plants!

If a Moon base was combined with industrial activities, then the profits made could pay towards the mission as a whole. One of the resources that could be mined is propellant (a chemical substance extracted from water ice at the Moon's poles, which could be used to fuel rockets). The fuel could then be sold to other space agencies for future space missions, such as trips to Mars. The ideal place for a Moon base would be at one of the Moon's poles – perhaps modelled on the US's Antarctic Station (the Amundsen-Scott South Pole Station) at Earth's South Pole.

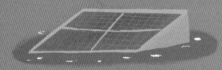

The most important resource available on the Moon is sunlight and its potential for solar power! Unlike the solar panels used on Earth, which can be affected by weather and of course night-time, solar collectors placed in orbit around the Moon would be able to collect energy from the Sun around the clock. Some scientists believe that the solar panels could be made in factories on the Moon, from the Moon's own resources. If this energy could be sold, it would contribute towards the costs of setting up a Moon base. It's thought that the solar panels could even be designed to make copies of themselves; which could then be sent into Earth orbit, providing power and electricity to all of us on Earth!

Many people in the space industry believe that setting up a Moon base is an important first step in achieving future manned missions to Mars. A Moon base would allow scientists to carry out scientific research and to test new technologies, before undertaking such a mission…

Reflections

...on a dusty ball of lifeless rock...

For most of us, the Moon still retains a quality of magic and mystery that means we will continue on our journey to understand it, explore it and perhaps, one day, inhabit it...

The Moon has had many different parts to play in a variety of cultures around the world… It's been the focal point of art and architecture, become the subject of songs, poetry and literature; and been at the centre stage of theatre and films – it's even performed live on television! It's led to myths about the Man in the Moon and the Moon Rabbit. It has even been worshipped as a god!

The Moon has inspired science-fiction stories, which in turn went on to inspire real-life events such as the development of rockets, leading to a full-on space race between some of the world's biggest and most powerful nations. It has been at the centre of debates, discussions and disputes.

Just as the Moon appears to change shape before our eyes, it has been subject to our changing views. On the one hand we associate it with birth and renewal; and on the other, we hold it responsible for people's erratic behaviour, illness and even death. Some of us have gone as far as not believing in it at all, accusing it of being a hologram…

The Moon is seen as having a dark, mysterious side, although even its dark side isn't that dark. The Moon has actually proved to be an essential tool, keeping Earth at just the right angle and assisting the tides of our oceans – in turn helping us to organise our time and calendars, and even setting body clocks in the animal world.

It was once viewed as heavenly and perfect, but the telescope enlightened us. In fact, scientists and thinkers have filled in many pieces of the jigsaw, exposing the Moon's hidden truths. Perhaps they are the ones who have shone real light on the Moon?

Humans have sent a whole trove of objects up to the Moon: hard landers, soft landers, orbiters, rockets, rovers, unmanned and manned – constantly probing and analysing our Moon. Brave astronauts have given their lives and animals have been sacrificed along the way… all in the name of science – yet will we ever really be satisfied?

The Moon isn't as invincible as we might like to think – it is getting older, shrinking and even developing wrinkles.

It's our closest neighbour in the solar system and it's even believed by some to be made up of parts of Earth. But our own Earth is just as magical… If you stood on the Moon's near side, you would also see Earth wax and wane and its many different phases.

But maybe we only appreciate the beauty of things from far away and don't always see the magic that's beneath our very noses…

"We came all this way to explore the Moon, and the most important thing is that we discovered the Earth."

– Astronaut William 'Bill' Anders (Apollo 8)

Glossary of Terms

apocalypse The end of the world

asteroid A small rocky body that orbits the Sun

astrononaut Someone who is trained to travel in space

astronomer Someone who studies space

atmosphere The mixture of gases that surround the Earth (or another planet)

axis An imaginary line that a given object rotates around

celestial body A natural object found outside the Earth's atmosphere (like the Moon, Sun or stars)

circadian Something that happens daily

circalunar Something that happens monthly

cosmonaut A Russian astronaut

decompression When gas gets into the blood

earthshine When sunlight reflected from Earth illuminates the darker portion of a crescent Moon

eclipse When light from one celestial body is blocked by another body coming between it and the source of its light

enlightenment The highest spiritual state possible, especially in the Buddhist religion; a state of huge insight and wisdom

epilepsy A medical condition that affects the brain and causes seizures

equinox The twice-yearly time when the the day and night are of equal length

eyespots Small areas on a palolo worm's tail that can detect moonlight

flyby probe A probe that is sent past a planet, flying close enough to record scientific data

fossil The remains of a prehistoric plant or animal preserved in rock

geologist Someone who studies the Earth's history through rocks

gibbous A Moon that is more than half but less than completely full

gravitational pull The attraction created by gravity

gravity The force that attracts something towards the centre of the Earth or towards any other physical body that has mass

intercalation When extra time is inserted into a calendar

lobate scarp A cliff that has formed on the Moon's crust

lunar Relating to the Moon

lunar libration When the Moon rocks slowly back and forth, showing us a slightly different angle

lunisolar To do with the combined movements or effects of the Sun and the Moon

maria Lava beds on the Moon's surface

melatonin A hormone that the body releases at night when it is dark

meteoroid A small rocky body found in outer space

molten Something made liquid by heat

moonquake tremors on the Moon's surface

naturalist Someone who studies the subject of natural history

neap A tide just after the first/third quarter of the Moon when there is the least difference between low and high water

oracle Someone who gives advice or a prophecy to the gods

orbit The regular course of a celestial body or spacecraft around a star or planet

paschal full Moon The first full Moon on or after 21st March

quarantine A state or place of isolation for people or animals who have been exposed to infectious diseases, in order to stop infection spreading

radiation A form of energy that comes from a nuclear reaction

radiation belt An area where charged energy particles are trapped by the Earth's magnetic field

rejuvenation Restoring someone or something to youth and vitality

retrograde orbit A clockwise orbit (usually things orbit anti-clockwise)

seismometer An instrument that measures and records earthquakes

solar Relating to the Sun

solar system A collection of planets and their moons in orbit around a sun

telescope An instrument designed to make distant things appear closer

ultraviolet A kind of short light wave produced by the Sun

waning The period when the visible part of the Moon is shrinking in the night sky

waxing The period when the visible part of the Moon is growing in the night sky

Glossary of People

Buzz Aldrin (1930 –)
Apollo 13 astronaut
Anaxagoras (born c. 510BCE)
philosopher
William 'Bill' Anders (1933–)
astronaut
Ludovico Ariosto (1474–1533) poet
Aristarchus of Samos (3rd century
BCE) Greek astronomer
Neil Armstrong (1930–2012)
first astronaut to walk on Moon

Jerome Beatty Jr (1916–2002)
author
Wilhelm Beer (1797–1850)
amateur astronomer
Tycho Brahe (1546–1601)
astronomer and writer
Wernher von Braun (1912–1977)
aerospace engineer

M. Scott Carpenter (1925–2013)
Project Mercury astronaut
Arthur C. Clarke (1917–2008)
author
Michael Collins (1930–)
Apollo 13 astronaut
Christopher Columbus (1451–1506)
navigator and explorer
L. Gordon Cooper (1927–2004)
Project Mercury astronaut

Louis Daguerre (1787–1851)
artist and photographer

Charles Darwin (1809–1882)
naturalist known for the theory
of evolution
George Darwin (1845–1912)
astronomer and mathematician
Walt Disney (1901–1966)
animator and film producer
John William Draper (1811–1882)
scientist and photographer

Yuri Gagarin (1934–1968)
first cosmonaut to journey to
outer space
Galileo Galilei (1564–1642)
scientist and astronomer
Gerald Gardner (1884–1964)
Wiccan, known as 'the father of
modern witchcraft'
Sally Gardner (1954–)
children's author
Theodor Giesel (1904–1991)
author, known as Dr Seuss
John Glenn (1921–2016)
Project Mercury astronaut
Robert H. Goddard (1882–1945)
engineer and inventor
Virgil I. 'Gus' Grissom (1926–1967)
Project Mercury astronaut

Asaph Hall (1829–1907)
astronomer
Thomas Harriot (1560–1621)
astronomer and mathematician
Johannes Hevelius (1611–1687)
astronomer

Moon Hoon (1968–)
architect

John F. Kennedy (1917–1963)
35th President of USA
Johannes Keppler (1571–1630)
astronomer and mathematician
Sergei Korolev (1907–1966)
rocket engineer

Fritz Lang (1890–1976)
filmmaker
William Lassell (1799–1880)
astronomer
Alexey Leonov (1934–)
cosmonaut
Henry Wadsworth Longfellow
(1807–1882)
poet and educator

Georges Méliès (1861–1938)
illusionist and filmmaker
Dr Charles Muses (1919–2000)
philosopher

Sir Isaac Newton (1643–1727)
scientist who discovered the laws
of gravity
Richard M. Nixon (1913–1994)
37th President of USA

George Pal (1908–1980)
film director and producer
Irving Pichel (1891–1954)
actor and film director

Georges Remi (1907–1983)
cartoonist, known as Hergé
Giovanni Riccioli (1598–1671)
astronomer

Walter Schirra (1923–2007)
Project Mercury astronaut
Johann Schröter (1745–1816)
astronomer
William Shakespeare (1564–1616)
playwright and actor
Alan Shepard (1923–1998)
Project Mercury astronaut
Donald 'Deke' Slayton (1924–
1993)
Project Mercury astronaut

Valentina Tereshkova (1937–)
first female cosmonaut in space
Konstantin Tsiolkovsky (1857–
1935)
rocket scientist

Harold Urey (1893–1981)
physical chemist

Jules Verne (1828–1905)
author

H.G. Wells (1866–1946)
author